200 Puzzles!

Sudoku

The Number Puzzle Sweeping The Nation!

#3

Published by Playmore Inc., Publishers,
and Waldman Publishing Corp., New York, New York

Printed in Canada

GETTING STARTED

Each sudoku puzzle is a 9 by 9 grid of horizontal and vertical rows, evenly separated into 9 squares with 9 spaces each. Instead of word clues, each puzzle's solution is determined by the pattern of the numbers already filled in. You solve the puzzle by filling in the missing digits so that, when completed, each row and each square will have all the numbers from 1 to 9; each number will appear in exactly nine spaces within each puzzle.

All three elements of the sudoku puzzle must be considered simultaneously: the horizontal rows, the vertical rows, and the 9 squares. You need to fill in each square with the numbers 1 through 9, but their location depends on where along each vertical and horizontal row these numbers already appear. Remember each number can be filled in only once on each horizontal and each vertical line.

Start by examining the "clues"–those numbers already filled in. They determine where each of the other numbers may and, more importantly, may not be filled in. Often by using a process of elimination, you can rule out where certain numbers can't go and thereby narrow the choices for where they can go. It isn't necessary to start with the number 1 or even with the first square, but rather wi the number that appears most frequently in any given sudoku, since you will find it easier to narrow down the remaining spaces in which i will appear in.

As you work through each puzzle, the final numbers will come more easily, and give you the experience needed for the progressively harder puzzles you'll encounter as you work your way through the book.

Enjoy!

easy

SUDOKU #1

3	8		4		5		7	9
1								2
			2		3			
	9	3	5		8	2	4	
	5	1	9		4	7	3	
			8		6			
9								7
6	2		3		7		8	4

easy

SUDOKU #2

			7		4	2		
3	4		1			5		
	5							1
1						3	6	
			2		8			
	7	6						9
9							3	
		1			5		9	2
		2	6		9			

easy

SUDOKU #3

2	1		9	4				8
9			1					
6	8		7	2	3			
3	5					8		
8								4
		2					5	9
			6	5	4		9	2
					1			6
1				3	9		8	5

easy

SUDOKU #4

8	1	7		2				
2						1		4
		3	5					
7				8		2		3
		8				7		
6		5		7				9
					7	4		
9		2						5
				3		6	2	7

easy

SUDOKU #5

		8	2				6	7
			3					
2			8	4			9	
4					9		7	
1		9				5		8
	2		5					9
	1			7	3			5
					5			
5	7				8	3		

easy

SUDOKU #6

	9		1	8		6		2
5	7		6			9		
	1		9					
			7		1			
	3						4	
			3		8			
					6		1	
		2			7		6	8
4		1		3	9		5	

easy

SUDOKU #7

2			9		8			3
		4				5		
	8		4		2		1	
4	5	8				2	7	1
1	3	9				6	5	4
	7		5		4		9	
		1				8		
8			3		6			2

easy

SUDOKU #8

5	3			7				8
8			5		2	4		3
2							1	
	5		4		1			
				3				
			2		5		8	
	2							7
6		5	9		7			1
3				4			2	6

easy

SUDOKU #9

5	9		1				2	
					2			7
3		2		7	5	4		1
					3			
6	5						1	2
			8					
2		6	7	3		9		8
9			2					
	4				9		6	3

easy

SUDOKU #10

	1	9		7			3	
3							6	4
2	6		3					
8			7					9
			2	4	5			
7					9			5
					7		4	1
4	9							2
	7			5		6	8	

easy

SUDOKU #11

		8			3		5	4
		6	5					
		9			8			
8				5	6	4		
6		7	2		9	5		8
		4	8	3				7
			3			1		
					7	6		
2	4		9			7		

easy

SUDOKU #12

6				3				
2		8	4					
3		1					5	4
							8	9
	2	3		6		7	1	
7	8							
8	9					5		7
					3	6		2
				9				8

easy

SUDOKU #13

4							7	1
2			5	3				6
3	9				6			
7		1		8				
			9		2			
				6		1		3
			3				6	9
5				9	8			2
8	6							7

easy

SUDOKU #14

			9					
8	4			2	3		1	
1	9		6		7			4
4		8					6	
			2		9			
	6					1		7
2			3		6		5	1
	3		8	1			9	6
					2			

easy

SUDOKU #15

	6		5		7		2	
	9						3	
8		4				7		1
3	1	5	7		8	9	4	6
6	8	9	1		4	5	7	2
9		8				4		7
	2						6	
	4		8		3		1	

easy

SUDOKU #16

	2	5		1	8	7		
1					7		2	3
	7						9	
8		2	7		6			
			4		1	3		9
	5						3	
7	4		2					8
		1	3	8		2	5	

easy

SUDOKU #17

6	4				3	1		8
5				8	9	3		7
								9
				2	7			
4				5				1
			3	1				
1								
9		5	2	3				4
8		2	6				9	3

easy

SUDOKU #18

	6					5		
5			3			4	9	
		2					3	
	7			3			4	5
4			5		6			9
8	1			2			6	
	3					6		
	5	6			9			3
		7					1	

easy

SUDOKU #19

3			5		7	4		
			1				2	7
8					6	1		
	1				5			
4				2				9
			8				5	
		8	6					3
9	4				1			
		7	4		8			1

easy

SUDOKU #20

9	2	8	7	3		4		
	7							3
			2		5		8	
6	3				2			
				9				
			8				7	4
	5		6		4			
1							4	
		4		5	8	1	6	7

easy

SUDOKU #21

7	8	9	2		3			
5			8		4	6		2
2		7					1	
	3	8				9	2	
	4					8		6
3		6	4		1			8
			9		6	3	5	1

easy

SUDOKU #22

1		6	8		3	7		4
		5				1		
			4		9			
4		8	9		5	3		1
9		1	2		6	8		7
			7		2			
		4				6		
3		7	5		1	2		8

easy

SUDOKU #23

1	7				4			
				6		9		
	4	8		9				
3			8	7				1
	8	4				3	5	
7				2	3			8
				8		5	7	
		2		3				
			6				8	3

easy

SUDOKU #24

				2	3	7		
7							1	5
9					7	6		
1					6			4
			2		4			
8			7					2
		5	1					7
3	4							9
		9	6	3				

easy

SUDOKU #25

1	9		7					
6		3	4			7		
7		5					3	8
	5					9		
3		1	5		9	6		2
		6					5	
8	6					1		5
		9			7	8		4
					6		9	3

easy

SUDOKU #26

5	6	3	8		4		9	
	4			9	5			
							8	
		8		4	3	9		
	7						5	
		4	7	6		2		
	3							
			3	2			4	
	8		4		6	5	3	1

easy

SUDOKU #27

5		7						6
		8				4		
3	2				6		9	
	9		1	2				
8								7
				5	7		2	
	5		9				7	4
		3				6		
4						1		8

easy

SUDOKU #28

		3		7				
		8			4	1	7	5
		5	9		2			3
7						3	4	
	4	9						6
9			8		3	4		
6	3	2	4			7		
				6		2		

easy

SUDOKU #29

	2	5			3		9	
6	9		4					
1						6		
3		7	6	2				1
4				1	8	7		2
		2						6
					6		7	8
	8		1			3	5	

easy

SUDOKU #30

7	9					8	1	
		4			2	9		
6			1			4		3
		6			7			4
		9				7		
2			8			5		
8		7			3			9
		1	7			2		
	4	5					7	1

easy

SUDOKU #31

	4			1	8	2		
	5		7					9
6		7			9	1		
2	3				6			
			8				2	1
		2	3			8		6
3					1		7	
		4	9	8			5	

easy

SUDOKU #32

			3	4	2			1
2		4	8				5	
3				9		4		
1		8						
	2			7			8	
						2		3
		1		8				2
	7				6	8		9
8			7	1	9			

easy

SUDOKU #33

1	3	6	9				5	
	7							8
2	9				3			6
			7		6			
		2				7		
			4		2			
9			2				6	7
5							3	
	8				9	2	4	1

easy

SUDOKU #34

		8	5	1	6	7		
7								
1						2		4
			7		1			2
		5	8	4	2	1		
2			3		5			
9		3						6
								1
		1	4	5	3	8		

easy

SUDOKU #35

7	6			4		9		
3	2			5				
	1	9		7	6			
	3	6						
4			2	8	3			7
						8	5	
			1	2		5	7	
				6			4	1
		7		3			6	9

easy

SUDOKU #36

9				2	4		7	
2			8	1				
8	3							5
3					9			
	8						4	
			2					1
5							3	7
				5	3			4
	7		4	6				2

easy

SUDOKU #37

2		6	4	1			5	
			8			9	2	
8								1
6	8			4				
		3		9		4		
				3			7	8
4								5
	6	9			4			
	5			8	2	3		6

easy

SUDOKU #38

					8		9	6
2	9	3					4	
	5			8		9		4
6				5				1
4		1		6			2	
	4					5	1	7
5	7		2					

easy

SUDOKU #39

	6			5			7	
1				8	6	3		
3				2	4		5	
7								8
	4						2	
5								3
	1		3	9				4
		7	2	1				5
	8			4			9	

easy

SUDOKU #40

	3		5				2	7
	5		4					
7			8	1				
	2					8	3	
4			2		1			9
	7	3					5	
				6	8			2
					7		6	
2	1				4		9	

easy

SUDOKU #41

5			2		3			9
	8		9		1		3	
		3				7		
6	7	1				3	2	5
3	2	4				9	7	8
		9				8		
	1		7		2		4	
4			6		5			1

easy

SUDOKU #42

6	3	5	1	9	4	2	8	7
2	4	8	7	3	6	9	5	1
9	1	7		5		3	4	6
	6	1	9	4	2	5	7	
	5	4	3		1	6	9	
	2	9	6	7	5	1	3	
5	9	2		1		8	6	3
4	8	6	5	2	3	7	1	9
1	7	3	8	6	9	4	2	5

easy

SUDOKU #43

1		8	4			6		5
	2		9					
			2	5				7
	5			1				
7								3
				2			6	
3				7	2			
					5		8	
6		2			4	7		1

easy

SUDOKU #44

	6		4			9		
	5	7		2				6
2				6	1			7
8	7							
4	3						7	5
							9	4
3			8	1				9
7				4		5	8	
		8			5		1	

easy

SUDOKU #45

	4	9	7		6	5	2	
	8						1	
6		3				9		4
2			4		8			9
9			3		5			2
5		8				7		1
	9						4	
	1	7	2		9	3	8	

easy

SUDOKU #46

	8	2		9	3			
		5	8					
		1	5			8		
	1		4			7		9
3								4
9		7			5		1	
		3			8	5		
					2	4		
			9	5		3	6	

easy

SUDOKU #47

1	9		2		8		7	
2			6					9
					7			6
			3	7		2	6	
4				9				7
	5	2		8	6			
3			7					
9					4			1
	7		8		1		9	2

easy

SUDOKU #48

	4					7		
			9	8				4
6		9			4	1		3
					5			
	3		6		2		5	
			3					
3		2	4			5		1
9				6	7			
		1					7	

easy

SUDOKU #49

	2	6				9	7	
3			7	8			5	
					2		6	4
				1			9	6
				7				
1	6			2				
6	5		2					
	8			9	4			7
	9	3				2	1	

easy

SUDOKU #50

6		8	3		4	2		9
			2		5			
9								5
	1	2	8		7	4	9	
	8	3	6		9	7	2	
8								2
			5		3			
2		6	7		1	5		4

easy

SUDOKU #51

			2				8	4
		6		4	9		5	
4					5	3	7	
9			5				2	1
2	5				7			8
	4	1	8					5
	8		3	5		2		
6	2				1			

easy

SUDOKU #52

7		5	2	8		6		
6		3						
			7					1
4				5		1	9	6
5								4
1	3	6		2				7
2					3			
						7		5
		4		9	1	2		8

easy

SUDOKU #53

4		8			5		3	7
	1		2				8	
								6
				7	2			5
7				5				9
2			4	1				
9								
	8				9		7	
3	5		6			4		8

easy

SUDOKU #54

4		2		7		5	8	
7		6	5					
	9		4					
9	7	4						8
5						2	3	7
					6		5	
					2	8		9
	3	8		5		4		1

easy

SUDOKU #55

8	5		6				4	
			3	8	4		1	
					1	6		
		9					7	
		2		3		5		
	1					2		
		6	4					
	3		5	7	9			
	4				6		2	3

easy

SUDOKU #56

		6		9				4
			2		3			
1	2	7	4					
5			1					7
7		1		4		5		2
9					6			3
					4	1	3	9
			6		5			
2				1		6		

easy

SUDOKU #57

	5	6	8				3	
2		9		1			5	
4					5			
7		3				9		
	2						8	
		8				1		2
			3					9
	6			4		5		7
	1				7	3	2	

easy

SUDOKU #58

7		9		5				8
3	4			1		7		
	1		9	7				
			5					9
	2	4				5	6	
1					9			
				9	3		7	
		7		8			2	6
8				2		1		3

easy

SUDOKU #59

6	9		5	3	8			1
		1				2		
3			4		2			
2		7		9		6		5
			6		7			9
		8				5		
4			9	6	3		8	7

easy

SUDOKU #60

	9		1	7			4	
7	4		3	9	6			
	1	3						
6								
		2		8		5		
								7
						3	6	
			7	3	2		9	8
	2			1	8		5	

easy

SUDOKU #61

2				7	6	5		
1		9		8		6		
3						2		
			7				9	
7								5
	9				1			
		2						8
		6		5		1		3
		4	1	6				7

easy

SUDOKU #62

		3	7	4				
4				1				2
1	7							5
8		9			3	5	1	
				9				
	4	5	1			8		9
5							4	6
2				5				8
				6	7	1		

easy

SUDOKU #63

	4	5		1			9	
				3	2		7	
	7		5				6	3
					3			9
	3			6			5	
6			9					
1	9				6		2	
	2		8	4				
	6			2		7	1	

easy

SUDOKU #64

	1	3	7		4	8		
5	8					6		
		9		8				5
		6						3
	2						6	
3						4		
9				2		7		
		4					8	2
		2	6		7	1	5	

easy

SUDOKU #65

6	3						8	4
8					6		5	
4				3		9		6
3		1						
			7		5			
						1		5
1		7		9				3
	6		2					9
9	4						1	7

easy

SUDOKU #66

2		8	1					6
7				6		5		
4	1		2					
		5				2		8
	2						6	
9		1				3		
					2		5	4
		9		4				3
8					1	6		7

easy

SUDOKU #67

8			1		4			
5			2				3	
	2	6		9			8	
	6							8
			5		9			
7							9	
	9			6		1	7	
	1				2			3
			7		5			9

easy

SUDOKU #68

6			4			7	2	
								9
3				6	5	8		1
5		7			4			
			7		6			
			2			5		7
7		3	5	2				6
4								
	9	8			1			5

easy

SUDOKU #69

6		4				8		
					1	3		6
2			7					
9		8	2		7			1
				8				
3			5		4	2		8
					5			4
7		3	4					
		1				6		7

easy

SUDOKU #70

			4	1	8			
3	2					7		
9								
7			2		1		8	
	4	1	7		3	5	2	
	8		9		4			7
								4
		2					5	3
			8	7	9			

easy

SUDOKU #71

7		8	4				2	
3	2			7				
						9	4	
8		9			2			
1			7		8			5
			5			6		9
	6	2						
				2			6	4
	7				5	1		2

easy

SUDOKU #72

		1				3		
	3	9	6		7	8	2	
6			2		4			7
8	9	7				5	3	1
3	4	6				7	8	2
2			8		5			9
	7	5	1		3	4	6	
		4				2		

easy

SUDOKU #73

2				8				
		5	7		1			
7			4			1		5
		6				7	4	1
9	1	2				6		
8		7			2			6
			5		4	9		
				1				3

easy

SUDOKU #74

	5		2		6			
4			9	7		1		
3	2							
8	4		3			5		
5	1						4	9
		7			4		1	8
							3	1
		2		9	8			4
			4		2		9	

easy

SUDOKU #75

5	9	8		1				
		2		4	3		8	
	1	4			6			
	4	6						
			3		5			
						7	9	
			4			5	1	
	3		5	9		4		
				3		2	6	9

easy

SUDOKU #76

7	1						3	2
5	6				2			
		8	3	7		5		
			5				2	1
8								4
1	3				4			
		5		4	1	9		
			7				5	6
6	8						4	7

easy

SUDOKU #77

7	3					9	5	1
						3		
1		4		6			2	
	4		8					
2	5		3		6		9	7
					7		1	
	2			3		1		5
		5						
6	1	9					3	2

easy

SUDOKU #78

	2	9	3				8	
7	3			4		2		
1	5				6			7
9						6		
6				9				5
		3						8
3			6				7	2
		2		7			5	4
	7				2	9	6	

easy

SUDOKU #79

4		6	8		7	9		1
	7		6		4		2	
5		8				4		7
		2				1		
			5		1			
		4				5		
9		3				2		8
	8		7		9		1	
2		7	1		3	6		9

easy

SUDOKU #80

8	2			5	9	3	7	
		7						
					6			4
					4	7		
4	5		9		7		2	8
		2	5					
2			3					
						8		
	8	5	2	7			4	9

easy

SUDOKU #81

		8		9		5	7	
	9			5		6		1
2								3
6			4	8		7		9
7		9		3	5			6
8								7
3		7		4			6	
	1	4		6		8		

easy

SUDOKU #82

	2	3	7			1		
5	9		3					
		6	2					5
9	4							
	6	8		1		9	5	
							6	8
8					3	2		
					6		4	1
		1			4	5	9	

easy

SUDOKU #83

5	2		7		3	6	4	
4			5					
		3	8				7	
9								3
			2		5			
8								6
	5				4	3		
					2			5
	1	7	3		9		2	4

easy

SUDOKU #84

	7		6		1		4	
			8		4			
	1	4				3	5	
6		3				5		9
1		9				8		2
	9	5				7	2	
			3		7			
	3		5		9		8	

easy

SUDOKU #85

2	9		5			6		
3	4						7	5
1	7			4				
9					8		2	
				6				
	5		4					8
				5			1	6
6	8						5	9
		7			9		4	3

easy

SUDOKU #86

		9	5	4				3
	6					5	4	
8								7
5		6	2			7		
		2				6		
		3			7	2		5
4								6
	2	8					5	
1				6	9	8		

easy

SUDOKU #87

7		6	8	4	1			3
	3			7				
5								7
9			6					
		7	2	1	4	8		
					9			4
6								8
				5			1	
4			3	2	6	7		5

easy

SUDOKU #88

1	6	5	3			7		
				4		8		
					9			6
				9			2	3
8								4
7	5			2				
9			8					
		6		5				
		8			3	1	6	2

easy

SUDOKU #89

	4			2	6			1
	2			5			7	
	1		3					5
	9	3				7		
	5						6	
		6				9	5	
4					2		9	
	7			9			3	
5			4	3			2	

easy

SUDOKU #90

5					3			
		3						8
	6		9	5	8	4		7
9				7	1			6
		6	5		2	9		
8			6	9				3
2		7	8	1	5		6	
6						7		
			2					1

easy

SUDOKU #91

3		2	8			4	7	
6					7			3
2		9	4	6				
4		5				1		9
				8	9	5		2
1			3					6
	2	6			8	7		1

easy

SUDOKU #92

6			1			8		
7				8	9			1
1						4		
		2		7		6		
3				5				2
		8		6		9		
		6						3
5			8	2				6
		1			7			8

easy

SUDOKU #93

3	6		9					
				6		5		1
5				1		6		
8		7	5		3	1		
		5	4		1	3		2
		2		3				5
4		9		7				
					9		2	3

easy

SUDOKU #94

				1	3	9	4	5
				9			7	
								3
5		2			7		6	9
1		7		4		5		2
9	6		3			4		7
7								
	9			5				
6	1	5	2	3				

easy

SUDOKU #95

4		9	1					
5		8		3	7			1
		1			4			
	6			8	3		5	
		5				2		
	8		2	5			7	
			9			7		
2			3	6		5		9
					1	6		2

easy

SUDOKU #96

6	7				8			
2				1	9	5	4	
						2		6
7		1		9		3		
		3		6		1		5
1		6						
	8	5	3	7				2
			4				5	9

easy

SUDOKU #97

	2		9			5		
3		4	2	5				
	7							
1		8			5	3		
5		9		1		7		8
		7	4			1		6
							4	
				8	2	6		7
		6			4		3	

easy

SUDOKU #98

		1	6		7	9		4
8				3		6	1	
3					4			
				5			7	6
		8				3		
6	7			9				
			3					7
	3	9		2				8
7		5	1		9	4		

easy

SUDOKU #99

	4	1	8	2		6		
5			1					7
	3			4				
			4				9	
9			2		7			5
	2				9			
				5			8	
8					4			2
		4		7	8	1	3	

easy

SUDOKU #100

		7			1	8	5	3
8	1							
3					2			
	5					3		6
	4		7		6		8	
6		9					1	
			4					8
							3	1
2	7	8	9			6		

easy

SUDOKU #101

8			3			9		1
3					8			
5			2	7				
		2	8		5			3
		5				1		
7			1		3	2		
				3	6			5
			9					7
9		3			2			8

easy

SUDOKU #102

		6	4		5		2	
			3	9	2			
3				6				
7		4	9					6
2								8
8					6	2		3
				8				2
			2	5	4			
	1		6		3	5		

easy

SUDOKU #103

9	7		4					
	2	6		5				9
							5	
5	6		7	8				1
		8				2		
2				1	4		9	6
	5							
3				7		6	4	
					1		2	7

easy

SUDOKU #104

		1	6	2		5		
		5					9	
7	8		5				3	
	6		3		1		2	
5								3
	3		9		5		1	
	5				4		7	6
	9					8		
		4		3	8	2		

easy

SUDOKU #105

	8			5	4		2	
7		6		9	2			
5	2							
6		2					9	
8								4
	5					8		1
							7	8
			2	4		9		5
	9		8	7			4	

easy

SUDOKU #106

8			3				4	7
	5		9					1
6			8		2	3		
	7	6						2
4						6	7	
		9	7		4			3
7					5		2	
1	8				3			6

easy

SUDOKU #107

	4		3		1	9		
9		6		8				
	7			6				
	9	8		1		7	4	
	2	5		7		1	8	
				4			9	
				9		3		6
		9	2		6		5	

easy

SUDOKU #108

		7				6		8
	9			6	3		2	5
			9					
	4		8			5		
		1	5		2	4		
		5			9		3	
					8			
6	2		3	1			8	
1		4				9		

easy

SUDOKU #109

8		4			6	5		
6					9	8		
				8			3	2
7							2	
2		9				4		1
	1							3
3	4			6				
		7	2					9
		8	1			2		5

easy

SUDOKU #110

9		4	5	3			2	
6			1			3	8	
		6	3			2	1	
				5				
	2	3			9	7		
	5	7			1			4
	4			2	3	8		6

easy

SUDOKU #111

1		5		7	3			2
3		4	2					
2		8		1	4			
7				3		5		
			1		6			
		6		8				9
			9	5		8		7
					7	4		5
5			3	4		6		1

easy

SUDOKU #112

	4	3		1	6	5		
8	5				9		2	
9			3					
5						6		7
1		6						2
					8			4
	2		6				7	8
		8	1	4		2	5	

easy

SUDOKU #113

6					7			
		1	5					8
3		5		8				
8	3			9				2
	1	4				6	5	
7				6			1	3
				3		4		7
4					2	1		
			6					5

easy

SUDOKU #114

1		8	2	4			7	
						9		
5					9	8		1
4			5					
8			4	1	2			6
					3			5
9		1	8					4
		5						
	8			5	6	1		9

easy

SUDOKU #115

	7	3		8		9		
		8	5	3		6		
6			4			1		
			3	1				7
		6				2		
7				9	5			
		2			8			1
		7		5	3	8		
		5		4		7	3	

easy

SUDOKU #116

	4		3			5		8
				7				
		7	6	5	1		9	
2			5				3	6
6		1				9		4
4	8				6			2
	1		2	4	9	3		
				3				
9		2			5		4	

easy

SUDOKU #117

		2		6				7
6		4			3			
	1		8	2			3	6
2	8	3				7		
		6				9	5	3
3	5			7	2		1	
			3			8		9
7				8		3		

easy

SUDOKU #118

7			6	3		1		
9				8	7	5		
		8				4		
3		5						
			1	9	3			
						6		3
		1				7		
		6	9	1				2
		3		5	6			4

easy

SUDOKU #119

	1	5				4	8	
9	3						2	5
			9		5			
2	8		4		6		1	7
7	9		2		3		5	6
			1		2			
1	7						3	4
	5	6				2	9	

easy

SUDOKU #120

2	4							5
5		9	7	2		8		
	1						7	
	2		9	5				
6		5				9		7
				7	3		6	
	5						3	
		6		3	7	1		8
8							2	6

mild

SUDOKU #121

7	3		6	2				
2		9			3		1	
			4	8		2		
					5		8	
	6						4	
	9		7					
		3		9	8			
	1		3			8		2
				4	6		9	3

mild

SUDOKU #122

	7		5					
2	9	6						
1				2		8	6	3
6	1			5		9		
	2			8			7	
		5		9			2	6
9	6	1		7				5
						6	1	7
					4		8	

mild

SUDOKU #123

6	4	2	1	5				
8						7		
		9		8				
1	3		2					
2			6	4	8			1
					3		7	2
				9		1		
		6						9
				2	4	5	8	6

mild

SUDOKU #124

7	4	1			6			
6	3			1				
8								1
2				7			1	
		8	1		4	2		
	6			5				8
5								6
				4			7	3
			3			8	2	9

mild

SUDOKU #125

	2		1		4	6		
		4						9
						4		7
1				6	3		2	
		2	9		5	3		
	3		7	8				6
4		3						
2						7		
		5	2		9		3	

mild

SUDOKU #126

4	7		8		1	6		3
5	3							1
			6				2	
9					6	2		
	6			2			5	
		7	1					6
	1				8			
8							6	9
7		9	2		3		8	5

mild

SUDOKU #127

9	4	3			5			
				6				
			7	1				5
					9	8		2
3								7
1		7	4					
4				9	6			
				3				
			5			9	7	8

mild

SUDOKU #128

	3			8	5			
	4			6	2	1		
							6	4
						3	4	
2			5		6			9
	6	7						
3	8							
		6	2	9			3	
			6	7			2	

mild

SUDOKU #129

	8		7		6		1	9
						5		4
			4	5				
7		1					9	
3	5			1			2	6
	2					4		1
				3	5			
8		6						
5	9		6		1		3	

mild

SUDOKU #130

6	7	9	2				1	
1					7			5
		5		3				
4		6						
		3				9		
						4		8
				5		8		
2			9					6
	9				6	1	2	3

mild

SUDOKU #131

			2					4
7		9				6	5	
	4		6					
6			9			5		
1	9			5			7	2
		5			3			6
					9		3	
	5	1				7		8
2					7			

mild

SUDOKU #132

		5	3	9				
								8
		9	4			1		
	8			2	1			4
6				5				2
2			9	6			5	
		6			8	3		
1								
				3	9	4		

mild

SUDOKU #133

			6			4	8	
	8	2						
5				1		6	9	
				7		8		
	4	3				7	5	
		6		8				
	2	1		5				7
						3	2	
	6	5			7			

mild

SUDOKU #134

		5	4	1	6			
		4						1
			3	5				2
8		6					2	7
				7				
9	7					8		3
6				4	8			
3						9		
			2	9	3	6		

mild

SUDOKU #135

8	6	9					7	
			7				5	
				8	2	4		
	9					2		
	4		1		5		6	
		6					9	
		1	5	3				
	8				7			
	3					1	4	7

mild

SUDOKU #136

6			1		5			8
		2				5		
9		1		6				
	6		7	1			5	
	4	7				2	3	
	9			5	3		7	
				7		1		2
		9				3		
4			5		1			7

mild

SUDOKU #137

	1	2	6					
8	4		2					
9				4			6	
3			1					7
		4		3		5		
2					5			8
	8			1				3
					9		8	4
					2	1	7	

mild

SUDOKU #138

		6	1		7			
3	5					4		
	7				3			1
	1	8	6		4			
9								5
			3		9	7	1	
6			9				3	
		2					7	9
			4		1	2		

mild

SUDOKU #139

8	2	1	6			5		
				7		9		
9			4		2			
7			2				8	
	6			4			5	
	4				1			9
			9		4			6
		7		8				
		2			7	3	9	4

mild

SUDOKU #140

9		7	2			5		
2					1			
			5				8	2
3		9		8				
	4						5	
				3		1		8
8	3				4			
			1					5
		2			7	8		6

mild

SUDOKU #141

9			2			3	8	
	6		5	3	9			
2				8				
1		9					4	
	3	4				9	7	
	7					1		5
				5				3
			4	6	3		9	
	8	6			2			7

mild

SUDOKU #142

	6	5		8				
7					4			
2		8		9		4		
		2					1	9
9		4				2		8
1	8					5		
		6		2		3		7
			4					2
				3		8	9	

mild

SUDOKU #143

		7	2	5		9		
3		5	9					
								4
4	7		6		8		2	
5								3
	1		7		5		9	6
2								
					2	8		5
		1		8	4	3		

mild

SUDOKU #144

				7	6		8	4
6					1	9	3	
			3					
7		1			4			
	6	4				1	9	
			5			7		6
					8			
	5	3	4					7
8	4		6	5				

mild

SUDOKU #145

		5		1	2	6		4
2					5			
			7	8		5		
4				9	7		2	6
7	8		6	5				9
		1		7	9			
			8					1
3		7	5	6		9		

mild

SUDOKU #146

	2	7			9		5	
5			7	6				
9				2				
3					2	8		
6								9
		8	1					6
				7				8
				4	6			3
	7		3			5	6	

mild

SUDOKU #147

	6				3	7		
8			5			1	2	
					2			4
		1		4		6	8	
	9						1	
	4	7		1		5		
7			2					
	2	9			1			8
		5	7				4	

mild

SUDOKU #148

1		7		2	5		6	
2	6			4		1		
		5						4
4		3						
			9	5	7			
						2		7
5						4		
		4		9			7	2
	2		6	8		3		1

mild

SUDOKU #149

8		6	5				2	
				9			5	
2	9			7				8
		3			9	4		
		8	1			7		
5				4			3	1
	7			2				
	2				1	8		5

mild

SUDOKU #150

		3	5	1				6
5								
	8		7	2				3
	1					9	8	
				7				
	7	8					1	
1				4	6		3	
								2
4				8	1	7		

mild

SUDOKU #151

	3			6	9			2
			2	3				4
					1	7		9
		2	8				4	1
	5						7	
9	4				5	3		
7		5	1					
4				7	6			
8			3	5			1	

mild

SUDOKU #152

				8	3	5		
7						3		4
		3	5					8
				9	2		4	5
	9			6			2	
2	4		1	3				
8					4	6		
1		4						9
		6	9	1				

mild

SUDOKU #153

			9		3		8	
8	6		2					
9				5			1	
					8		6	2
	3						9	
2	7		5					
	2			9				4
					5		7	1
	5		3		1			

mild

SUDOKU #154

4			9		3	2	7	
			1			6	8	
		7						
		1	2					6
		3				1		
2					5	8		
						7		
	7	5			8			
	4	9	5		1			8

mild

SUDOKU #155

1	5		2				6	4
	8		3					
7				5		3		
5						7		
6			4		5			2
		1						3
		8		2				6
					1		8	
4	2				6		9	7

mild

SUDOKU #156

		2		5	8			
5		7	1					4
8							5	6
1			7					
4				8				2
					9			7
9	2							1
6					2	7		8
			8	3		2		

mild

SUDOKU #157

	6			8		3	2	
7		4					8	
			5			4		1
					8			7
3	8						9	4
6			2					
9		2			4			
	1					9		2
	7	8		3			4	

mild

SUDOKU #158

	2	1		9		7		
			8			5	3	
6					2			
		5					8	7
7		6				9		5
2	8					4		
			4					1
	4	7			8			
		8		7		6	4	

mild

SUDOKU #159

1	3			9				8
9		5	7		2			
						9		
8				4	7			
5								3
			9	2				1
		6						
			6		4	5		7
7				3			1	6

mild

SUDOKU #160

	7			5		4		
9			1			8		
				3	9			1
3							8	
	4		9		7		5	
	5							2
2			8	1				
		5			2			7
		3		6			1	

mild

SUDOKU #161

				9	5		6	4
		5					3	8
	4		1				5	
			7	6		4		
		4				2		
		8		1	9			
	5				3		9	
8	7					3		
2	3		9	5				

mild

SUDOKU #162

3	6		5					
5			1	6	3			9
		7						
				2				8
7		8				3		6
2				1				
						6		
6			2	5	8			7
					9		8	1

mild

SUDOKU #163

					9			5
5	4			1	7			
							9	8
	5	1		9		8		
2								6
		3		4		2	1	
7	6							
			6	2			7	4
3			7					

mild

SUDOKU #164

9		6		4			8	
1					6			
5					8	4		
7	1	2	4					
					1	9	7	3
		3	1					9
			6					8
	4			3		6		2

mild

SUDOKU #165

9	2			6		4		
		8				7	1	
				3				6
3		1	2				7	
	8				7	5		9
2				4				
	6	7				8		
		4		7			3	2

mild

SUDOKU #166

				6	7		4	1
5		7		3				8
			2			7		
						9		2
	3		1		6		8	
8		1						
		5			8			
2				9		8		7
7	9		3	1				

mild

SUDOKU #167

				3	6	7	9	4
8					9	6	1	
4								
	5		2			9		
			3		7			
		2			5		8	
								1
	8	1	5					9
3	6	7	9	1				

mild

SUDOKU #168

7		6	4					
1		5	8					
8				9				5
				5	1			
	2	8				9	3	
			9	3				
6				8				2
					6	5		3
					3	7		9

ambitious **SUDOKU #169**

		2	1	5				
	4	6	7					
9				2			6	
			5				1	3
2				8				7
1	6				3			
	3			4				8
					7	4	3	
				3	5	9		

ambitious **SUDOKU #170**

4				9			5	
6			7	2		8		
8			4	5				1
3						1		
	5						9	
		2						3
2				8	9			6
		3		1	7			2
	8			4				5

ambitious SUDOKU #171

		6		2			1	9
	5	2				8	4	
								6
4	2		7	3				
		7	8		4	1		
				9	2		7	4
2								
	7	5				4	8	
3	4			8		2		

ambitious SUDOKU #172

		7	2			1	4	
						9	2	
8					3			6
2			7	4		6		
			9		2			
		8		5	6			9
3			6					2
	7	6						
	1	2			7	8		

ambitious **SUDOKU #173**

		3	7	9		1		
	2		5					
4	7						9	
9					2		3	
		6				4		
	1		6					2
	8						4	9
					7		6	
		1		3	8	2		

ambitious **SUDOKU #174**

	3				9			
		1	5			7	2	
			3					
7		5			8			4
		2		1		5		
8			7			2		6
					1			
	2	7			5	4		
			8				9	

ambitious **SUDOKU #175**

1				9				
6					7			
		9	8				7	
3			7			2		5
	7			3			8	
4		1			9			3
	3				6	9		
			1					2
				4				6

ambitious **SUDOKU #176**

	8	9		4	3	6		
	1		9					
2				8	5			
	9	3	4	2				
6								8
				3	6	9	2	
			3	9				6
					4		8	
		8	6	7		3	1	

ambitious SUDOKU #177

8	4	3			9	2		
	1		2					
5	2		1					
		9			8			1
			6		7			
1			9			8		
					1		2	7
					6		4	
		1	4			3	6	5

ambitious SUDOKU #178

		7	4					
				9	7			
1			6	8			7	9
4				7				6
7	6						1	8
8				1				2
5	3			4	8			1
			5	6				
					3	6		

ambitious **SUDOKU #179**

	5	3						
	4			6	2			
		9	3				5	6
5			8			6		
3		6		7		8		1
		1			6			5
8	3				4	1		
			7	1			8	
						9	6	

ambitious **SUDOKU #180**

			8		5	3		
3			1	7		9		
9	7		4		6			
7			3			5		
	1						2	
		5			7			3
			7		4		3	6
		7		8	1			5
		4	6		3			

ambitious **SUDOKU #181**

4			3	2				6
						1		
6		5				4		
8	7		5			9		
				4				
		9			2		1	8
		4				6		9
		3						
9				6	7			2

ambitious **SUDOKU #182**

		5	7		8	6		9
	3	7		6				
					5		7	
	8							6
		3	5		9	1		
7							9	
	7		2					
				4		7	2	
4		8	3		7	5		

ambitious **SUDOKU #183**

6		3	4	8			7	
8			6					
	5	4			1			
	7					9		2
				5				
9		6					4	
			7			4	8	
					2			6
	1			6	4	2		9

ambitious **SUDOKU #184**

	8	3				5	6	
					6			
6				8				1
		2		5	7	6		
5								2
		9	4	3		8		
2				4				6
			1					
	9	5				3	2	

tough

SUDOKU #185

			1	9	4	2		
5	4				2			9
2							9	
1	9			3			6	7
	5							3
6			9				7	5
		4	8	5	7			

tough

SUDOKU #186

3			9					
6		7					1	
				5	4	6		
	3	5			9			
2								6
			2			1	7	
		2	6	8				
	6					7		4
					3			9

tough

SUDOKU #187

		5	7		6	2	9	
4				2				
7			1					5
						1	7	6
		3				5		
5	7	2						
2					9			7
				6				8
	5	9	3		7	4		

tough

SUDOKU #188

	2		6			8	1	
								6
8		6		5			4	2
4			3	1	5			
			2	9	7			5
2	8			6		3		4
1								
	4	5			9		6	

tough

SUDOKU #189

	5		9			4	8	
4			3		7		9	1
9				4				
		5					4	
	7						5	
	3					1		
				8				6
7	6		5		1			4
	1	3			9		7	

tough

SUDOKU #190

2		3		9	8			
9								
6				2	3	7		
		1	3					8
	9			4			1	
3					5	6		
		2	4	5				6
								1
			7	3		5		4

tough

SUDOKU #191

				9		3		
1				8				
2	7	9	6					
6	3	7		4				1
8				5		2	3	7
					5	7	8	4
				6				2
		5		1				

tough

SUDOKU #192

5	2			9	8			
7								
			6	5			3	
			3					7
2		6				5		1
9					2			
	7			6	9			
								6
			4	2			5	9

very tough **SUDOKU #193**

	1				6	4	3	
6					9			
	7	8			1			6
	4				3	2		
1								8
		2	7				4	
3			6			5	2	
			1					9
	2	1	8				6	

very tough **SUDOKU #194**

	4	1	3		6			
5			2	7				8
		7				2		
	8							6
3				6				2
1							5	
		3				1		
7				2	4			3
			6		3	9	2	

very tough **SUDOKU #195**

3	5		7					1
2		9	6					
					2	6		4
9					5		4	
		7				2		
	6		2					7
1		5	8					
					7	4		3
7					6		1	2

very tough **SUDOKU #196**

6					5		7	
7			4	6				
5		1		8	2			
	9	2			4			
			1		3			
			5			1	2	
			6	3		9		2
				4	7			5
	1		2					6

very tough SUDOKU #197

8		5		3	2	4		
3				7				
2			4				9	
1		3			4			
				8				
			1			7		2
	3				1			9
				6				8
		8	5	4		2		1

very tough SUDOKU #198

6	5		4				8	
					7			2
	7		9				6	
5						2		3
	1		2		5		4	
4		9						8
	3				9		2	
1			6					
	8				3		1	4

very tough SUDOKU #199

	3			4		6		1
1			5				3	8
		5			9			
4								
		9		6		7		
								5
			8			5		
3	9				7			6
5		7		1			2	

very tough SUDOKU #200

		1	3	7		5		
			2					8
	6	8			1			3
	1		8			9		
			7	4	9			
		9			6		5	
6			4			2	8	
7					2			
		2		9	7	4		

ANSWER KEY

SUDOKU #1

3	8	2	4	1	5	6	7	9
1	7	4	6	8	9	3	5	2
5	6	9	2	7	3	4	1	8
7	9	3	5	6	8	2	4	1
2	4	6	7	3	1	8	9	5
8	5	1	9	2	4	7	3	6
4	1	7	8	5	6	9	2	3
9	3	8	1	4	2	5	6	7
6	2	5	3	9	7	1	8	4

SUDOKU #2

6	1	9	7	5	4	2	8	3
3	4	8	1	9	2	5	7	6
2	5	7	3	8	6	9	4	1
1	2	5	9	4	7	3	6	8
4	9	3	2	6	8	1	5	7
8	7	6	5	1	3	4	2	9
9	6	4	8	2	1	7	3	5
7	8	1	4	3	5	6	9	2
5	3	2	6	7	9	8	1	4

SUDOKU #3

2	1	3	9	4	6	5	7	8
9	4	7	1	8	5	2	6	3
6	8	5	7	2	3	9	4	1
3	5	6	4	9	2	8	1	7
8	9	1	5	6	7	3	2	4
4	7	2	3	1	8	6	5	9
7	3	8	6	5	4	1	9	2
5	2	9	8	7	1	4	3	6
1	6	4	2	3	9	7	8	5

SUDOKU #4

8	1	7	9	2	4	5	3	6
2	5	9	7	6	3	1	8	4
4	6	3	5	1	8	9	7	2
7	9	1	4	8	5	2	6	3
3	4	8	6	9	2	7	5	1
6	2	5	3	7	1	8	4	9
1	3	6	2	5	7	4	9	8
9	7	2	8	4	6	3	1	5
5	8	4	1	3	9	6	2	7

SUDOKU #5

3	9	8	2	5	1	4	6	7
7	4	1	3	9	6	8	5	2
2	5	6	8	4	7	1	9	3
4	3	5	6	8	9	2	7	1
1	6	9	7	3	2	5	4	8
8	2	7	5	1	4	6	3	9
6	1	2	4	7	3	9	8	5
9	8	3	1	6	5	7	2	4
5	7	4	9	2	8	3	1	6

SUDOKU #6

3	9	4	1	8	5	6	7	2
5	7	8	6	2	4	9	3	1
2	1	6	9	7	3	5	8	4
6	2	5	7	4	1	8	9	3
8	3	7	5	9	2	1	4	6
1	4	9	3	6	8	7	2	5
7	8	3	2	5	6	4	1	9
9	5	2	4	1	7	3	6	8
4	6	1	8	3	9	2	5	7

SUDOKU #7

2	1	7	9	5	8	4	6	3
9	6	4	7	3	1	5	2	8
5	8	3	4	6	2	9	1	7
4	5	8	6	9	3	2	7	1
7	2	6	1	4	5	3	8	9
1	3	9	8	2	7	6	5	4
3	7	2	5	8	4	1	9	6
6	4	1	2	7	9	8	3	5
8	9	5	3	1	6	7	4	2

SUDOKU #8

5	3	1	6	7	4	2	9	8
8	6	9	5	1	2	4	7	3
2	7	4	8	9	3	6	1	5
7	5	2	4	8	1	3	6	9
4	8	6	7	3	9	1	5	2
9	1	3	2	6	5	7	8	4
1	2	8	3	5	6	9	4	7
6	4	5	9	2	7	8	3	1
3	9	7	1	4	8	5	2	6

SUDOKU #9

5	9	7	1	4	8	3	2	6
1	8	4	3	6	2	5	9	7
3	6	2	9	7	5	4	8	1
8	2	1	6	5	3	7	4	9
6	5	3	4	9	7	8	1	2
4	7	9	8	2	1	6	3	5
2	1	6	7	3	4	9	5	8
9	3	5	2	8	6	1	7	4
7	4	8	5	1	9	2	6	3

SUDOKU #10

5	1	9	4	7	6	2	3	8
3	8	7	5	9	2	1	6	4
2	6	4	3	1	8	5	9	7
8	2	5	7	6	3	4	1	9
9	3	1	2	4	5	8	7	6
7	4	6	1	8	9	3	2	5
6	5	3	8	2	7	9	4	1
4	9	8	6	3	1	7	5	2
1	7	2	9	5	4	6	8	3

SUDOKU #11

1	2	8	6	7	3	9	5	4
3	7	6	5	9	4	8	1	2
4	5	9	1	2	8	3	7	6
8	3	2	7	5	6	4	9	1
6	1	7	2	4	9	5	3	8
5	9	4	8	3	1	2	6	7
7	6	5	3	8	2	1	4	9
9	8	3	4	1	7	6	2	5
2	4	1	9	6	5	7	8	3

SUDOKU #12

6	4	9	7	3	5	8	2	1
2	5	8	4	1	9	3	7	6
3	7	1	6	2	8	9	5	4
1	6	5	3	7	2	4	8	9
9	2	3	8	6	4	7	1	5
7	8	4	9	5	1	2	6	3
8	9	2	1	4	6	5	3	7
4	1	7	5	8	3	6	9	2
5	3	6	2	9	7	1	4	8

SUDOKU #13

4	5	6	8	2	9	3	7	1
2	1	7	5	3	4	9	8	6
3	9	8	1	7	6	2	5	4
7	2	1	4	8	3	6	9	5
6	3	5	9	1	2	7	4	8
9	8	4	7	6	5	1	2	3
1	4	2	3	5	7	8	6	9
5	7	3	6	9	8	4	1	2
8	6	9	2	4	1	5	3	7

SUDOKU #14

6	5	3	9	4	1	8	7	2
8	4	7	5	2	3	6	1	9
1	9	2	6	8	7	5	3	4
4	2	8	1	7	5	9	6	3
3	7	1	2	6	9	4	8	5
5	6	9	4	3	8	1	2	7
2	8	4	3	9	6	7	5	1
7	3	5	8	1	4	2	9	6
9	1	6	7	5	2	3	4	8

SUDOKU #15

1	6	3	5	9	7	8	2	4
2	9	7	4	8	1	6	3	5
8	5	4	3	6	2	7	9	1
3	1	5	7	2	8	9	4	6
4	7	2	6	5	9	1	8	3
6	8	9	1	3	4	5	7	2
9	3	8	2	1	6	4	5	7
7	2	1	9	4	5	3	6	8
5	4	6	8	7	3	2	1	9

SUDOKU #16

3	2	5	9	1	8	7	6	4
1	8	9	6	4	7	5	2	3
4	7	6	5	3	2	8	9	1
8	3	2	7	9	6	1	4	5
9	1	4	8	5	3	6	7	2
5	6	7	4	2	1	3	8	9
2	5	8	1	7	9	4	3	6
7	4	3	2	6	5	9	1	8
6	9	1	3	8	4	2	5	7

SUDOKU #17

6	4	9	5	7	3	1	2	8
5	2	1	4	8	9	3	6	7
7	8	3	1	6	2	4	5	9
3	1	6	9	2	7	8	4	5
4	9	7	8	5	6	2	3	1
2	5	8	3	1	4	9	7	6
1	3	4	7	9	5	6	8	2
9	6	5	2	3	8	7	1	4
8	7	2	6	4	1	5	9	3

SUDOKU #18

3	6	4	2	9	8	5	7	1
5	8	1	3	6	7	4	9	2
7	9	2	1	4	5	8	3	6
6	7	9	8	3	1	2	4	5
4	2	3	5	7	6	1	8	9
8	1	5	9	2	4	3	6	7
9	3	8	7	1	2	6	5	4
1	5	6	4	8	9	7	2	3
2	4	7	6	5	3	9	1	8

SUDOKU #19

3	2	1	5	8	7	4	9	6
5	6	4	1	3	9	8	2	7
8	7	9	2	4	6	1	3	5
7	1	2	9	6	5	3	8	4
4	8	5	7	2	3	6	1	9
6	9	3	8	1	4	7	5	2
1	5	8	6	7	2	9	4	3
9	4	6	3	5	1	2	7	8
2	3	7	4	9	8	5	6	1

SUDOKU #20

9	2	8	7	3	6	4	5	1
4	7	5	1	8	9	6	2	3
3	6	1	2	4	5	7	8	9
6	3	9	4	7	2	5	1	8
8	4	7	5	9	1	2	3	6
5	1	2	8	6	3	9	7	4
7	5	3	6	1	4	8	9	2
1	8	6	9	2	7	3	4	5
2	9	4	3	5	8	1	6	7

SUDOKU #21

7	8	9	2	6	3	1	4	5
5	1	3	8	7	4	6	9	2
6	2	4	5	1	9	7	8	3
2	6	7	3	9	8	5	1	4
1	3	8	6	4	5	9	2	7
9	4	5	1	2	7	8	3	6
8	5	1	7	3	2	4	6	9
3	9	6	4	5	1	2	7	8
4	7	2	9	8	6	3	5	1

SUDOKU #22

1	9	6	8	5	3	7	2	4
8	4	5	6	2	7	1	3	9
7	3	2	4	1	9	5	8	6
4	2	8	9	7	5	3	6	1
6	7	3	1	8	4	9	5	2
9	5	1	2	3	6	8	4	7
5	8	9	7	6	2	4	1	3
2	1	4	3	9	8	6	7	5
3	6	7	5	4	1	2	9	8

SUDOKU #23

1	7	9	3	5	4	8	6	2
5	2	3	7	6	8	9	1	4
6	4	8	1	9	2	7	3	5
3	9	6	8	7	5	4	2	1
2	8	4	9	1	6	3	5	7
7	1	5	4	2	3	6	9	8
4	3	1	2	8	9	5	7	6
8	6	2	5	3	7	1	4	9
9	5	7	6	4	1	2	8	3

SUDOKU #24

4	1	6	5	2	3	7	9	8
7	3	2	9	6	8	4	1	5
9	5	8	4	1	7	6	2	3
1	2	7	3	5	6	9	8	4
5	9	3	2	8	4	1	7	6
8	6	4	7	9	1	3	5	2
6	8	5	1	4	9	2	3	7
3	4	1	8	7	2	5	6	9
2	7	9	6	3	5	8	4	1

SUDOKU #25

1	9	4	7	3	8	5	2	6
6	8	3	4	2	5	7	1	9
7	2	5	9	6	1	4	3	8
2	5	8	6	7	3	9	4	1
3	7	1	5	4	9	6	8	2
9	4	6	1	8	2	3	5	7
8	6	2	3	9	4	1	7	5
5	3	9	2	1	7	8	6	4
4	1	7	8	5	6	2	9	3

SUDOKU #26

5	6	3	8	1	4	7	9	2
8	4	7	2	9	5	1	6	3
2	9	1	6	3	7	4	8	5
1	2	8	5	4	3	9	7	6
6	7	9	1	8	2	3	5	4
3	5	4	7	6	9	2	1	8
4	3	6	9	5	1	8	2	7
7	1	5	3	2	8	6	4	9
9	8	2	4	7	6	5	3	1

SUDOKU #27

5	4	7	2	1	9	3	8	6
9	6	8	3	7	5	4	1	2
3	2	1	4	8	6	7	9	5
7	9	5	1	2	4	8	6	3
8	1	2	6	9	3	5	4	7
6	3	4	8	5	7	9	2	1
1	5	6	9	3	8	2	7	4
2	8	3	7	4	1	6	5	9
4	7	9	5	6	2	1	3	8

SUDOKU #28

1	6	3	5	7	8	9	2	4
2	9	8	6	3	4	1	7	5
4	7	5	9	1	2	6	8	3
7	8	6	1	5	9	3	4	2
5	2	1	3	4	6	8	9	7
3	4	9	2	8	7	5	1	6
9	5	7	8	2	3	4	6	1
6	3	2	4	9	1	7	5	8
8	1	4	7	6	5	2	3	9

SUDOKU #29

8	2	5	7	6	3	1	9	4
6	9	3	4	8	1	5	2	7
1	7	4	2	9	5	6	8	3
3	5	7	6	2	9	8	4	1
2	1	8	3	7	4	9	6	5
4	6	9	5	1	8	7	3	2
9	3	2	8	5	7	4	1	6
5	4	1	9	3	6	2	7	8
7	8	6	1	4	2	3	5	9

SUDOKU #30

7	9	2	6	3	4	8	1	5
1	3	4	5	8	2	9	6	7
6	5	8	1	7	9	4	2	3
5	8	6	9	2	7	1	3	4
4	1	9	3	5	6	7	8	2
2	7	3	8	4	1	5	9	6
8	2	7	4	1	3	6	5	9
3	6	1	7	9	5	2	4	8
9	4	5	2	6	8	3	7	1

SUDOKU #31

9	4	3	5	1	8	2	6	7
8	5	1	7	6	2	4	3	9
6	2	7	4	3	9	1	8	5
2	3	9	1	5	6	7	4	8
5	1	8	2	7	4	6	9	3
4	7	6	8	9	3	5	2	1
7	9	2	3	4	5	8	1	6
3	8	5	6	2	1	9	7	4
1	6	4	9	8	7	3	5	2

SUDOKU #32

5	8	7	3	4	2	6	9	1
2	9	4	8	6	1	3	5	7
3	1	6	5	9	7	4	2	8
1	5	8	6	2	3	9	7	4
6	2	3	9	7	4	1	8	5
7	4	9	1	5	8	2	6	3
9	6	1	4	8	5	7	3	2
4	7	5	2	3	6	8	1	9
8	3	2	7	1	9	5	4	6

SUDOKU #33

1	3	6	9	7	8	4	5	2
4	7	5	6	2	1	3	9	8
2	9	8	5	4	3	1	7	6
8	4	1	7	3	6	9	2	5
3	6	2	8	9	5	7	1	4
7	5	9	4	1	2	6	8	3
9	1	3	2	8	4	5	6	7
5	2	4	1	6	7	8	3	9
6	8	7	3	5	9	2	4	1

SUDOKU #34

4	2	8	5	1	6	7	9	3
7	3	9	2	8	4	6	1	5
1	5	6	9	3	7	2	8	4
8	6	4	7	9	1	3	5	2
3	9	5	8	4	2	1	6	7
2	1	7	3	6	5	9	4	8
9	4	3	1	2	8	5	7	6
5	8	2	6	7	9	4	3	1
6	7	1	4	5	3	8	2	9

SUDOKU #35

7	6	8	3	4	2	9	1	5
3	2	4	9	5	1	7	8	6
5	1	9	8	7	6	4	3	2
8	3	6	5	9	7	1	2	4
4	5	1	2	8	3	6	9	7
9	7	2	6	1	4	8	5	3
6	4	3	1	2	9	5	7	8
2	9	5	7	6	8	3	4	1
1	8	7	4	3	5	2	6	9

SUDOKU #36

9	5	1	3	2	4	8	7	6
2	6	7	8	1	5	4	9	3
8	3	4	9	7	6	2	1	5
3	1	6	5	4	9	7	2	8
7	8	2	6	3	1	5	4	9
4	9	5	2	8	7	3	6	1
5	4	8	1	9	2	6	3	7
6	2	9	7	5	3	1	8	4
1	7	3	4	6	8	9	5	2

SUDOKU #37

2	9	6	4	1	7	8	5	3
7	1	5	8	6	3	9	2	4
8	3	4	5	2	9	7	6	1
6	8	2	7	4	1	5	3	9
5	7	3	6	9	8	4	1	2
9	4	1	2	3	5	6	7	8
4	2	8	3	7	6	1	9	5
3	6	9	1	5	4	2	8	7
1	5	7	9	8	2	3	4	6

SUDOKU #38

8	6	4	9	2	1	7	5	3
7	1	5	3	4	8	2	9	6
2	9	3	6	7	5	1	4	8
3	5	7	1	8	2	9	6	4
6	2	9	4	5	3	8	7	1
4	8	1	7	6	9	3	2	5
9	4	2	8	3	6	5	1	7
5	7	8	2	1	4	6	3	9
1	3	6	5	9	7	4	8	2

SUDOKU #39

9	6	4	1	5	3	8	7	2
1	5	2	7	8	6	3	4	9
3	7	8	9	2	4	1	5	6
7	3	9	4	6	2	5	1	8
8	4	6	5	3	1	9	2	7
5	2	1	8	7	9	4	6	3
6	1	5	3	9	7	2	8	4
4	9	7	2	1	8	6	3	5
2	8	3	6	4	5	7	9	1

SUDOKU #40

8	3	4	5	9	6	1	2	7
9	5	1	4	7	2	3	8	6
7	6	2	8	1	3	9	4	5
6	2	9	7	4	5	8	3	1
4	8	5	2	3	1	6	7	9
1	7	3	6	8	9	2	5	4
3	4	7	9	6	8	5	1	2
5	9	8	1	2	7	4	6	3
2	1	6	3	5	4	7	9	8

SUDOKU #41

5	4	6	2	7	3	1	8	9
7	8	2	9	6	1	5	3	4
1	9	3	4	5	8	7	6	2
6	7	1	8	4	9	3	2	5
9	5	8	3	2	7	4	1	6
3	2	4	5	1	6	9	7	8
2	6	9	1	3	4	8	5	7
8	1	5	7	9	2	6	4	3
4	3	7	6	8	5	2	9	1

SUDOKU #42

6	3	5	1	9	4	2	8	7
2	4	8	7	3	6	9	5	1
9	1	7	2	5	8	3	4	6
3	6	1	9	4	2	5	7	8
7	5	4	3	8	1	6	9	2
8	2	9	6	7	5	1	3	4
5	9	2	4	1	7	8	6	3
4	8	6	5	2	3	7	1	9
1	7	3	8	6	9	4	2	5

SUDOKU #43

1	9	8	4	3	7	6	2	5
5	2	7	9	8	6	1	3	4
4	3	6	2	5	1	8	9	7
2	5	3	6	1	9	4	7	8
7	6	9	5	4	8	2	1	3
8	4	1	7	2	3	5	6	9
3	1	5	8	7	2	9	4	6
9	7	4	1	6	5	3	8	2
6	8	2	3	9	4	7	5	1

SUDOKU #44

1	6	3	4	5	7	9	2	8
9	5	7	3	2	8	1	4	6
2	8	4	9	6	1	3	5	7
8	7	2	5	9	4	6	3	1
4	3	9	1	8	6	2	7	5
5	1	6	2	7	3	8	9	4
3	4	5	8	1	2	7	6	9
7	2	1	6	4	9	5	8	3
6	9	8	7	3	5	4	1	2

SUDOKU #45

1	4	9	7	3	6	5	2	8
7	8	2	5	9	4	6	1	3
6	5	3	8	2	1	9	7	4
2	6	5	4	7	8	1	3	9
8	3	1	9	6	2	4	5	7
9	7	4	3	1	5	8	6	2
5	2	8	6	4	3	7	9	1
3	9	6	1	8	7	2	4	5
4	1	7	2	5	9	3	8	6

SUDOKU #46

6	8	2	7	9	3	1	4	5
4	3	5	8	6	1	9	2	7
7	9	1	5	2	4	8	3	6
2	1	8	4	3	6	7	5	9
3	5	6	1	7	9	2	8	4
9	4	7	2	8	5	6	1	3
1	7	3	6	4	8	5	9	2
5	6	9	3	1	2	4	7	8
8	2	4	9	5	7	3	6	1

SUDOKU #47

1	9	6	2	4	8	3	7	5
2	8	7	6	5	3	1	4	9
5	3	4	9	1	7	8	2	6
8	1	9	3	7	5	2	6	4
4	6	3	1	9	2	5	8	7
7	5	2	4	8	6	9	1	3
3	4	1	7	2	9	6	5	8
9	2	8	5	6	4	7	3	1
6	7	5	8	3	1	4	9	2

SUDOKU #48

1	4	8	2	3	6	7	9	5
7	5	3	9	8	1	6	2	4
6	2	9	7	5	4	1	8	3
2	9	7	8	4	5	3	1	6
8	3	4	6	1	2	9	5	7
5	1	6	3	7	9	2	4	8
3	7	2	4	9	8	5	6	1
9	8	5	1	6	7	4	3	2
4	6	1	5	2	3	8	7	9

SUDOKU #49

5	2	6	1	4	3	9	7	8
3	4	9	7	8	6	1	5	2
7	1	8	9	5	2	3	6	4
8	7	2	3	1	5	4	9	6
9	3	4	6	7	8	5	2	1
1	6	5	4	2	9	7	8	3
6	5	7	2	3	1	8	4	9
2	8	1	5	9	4	6	3	7
4	9	3	8	6	7	2	1	5

SUDOKU #50

6	5	8	3	7	4	2	1	9
3	4	1	2	9	5	6	8	7
9	2	7	1	6	8	3	4	5
5	1	2	8	3	7	4	9	6
7	6	9	4	1	2	8	5	3
4	8	3	6	5	9	7	2	1
8	3	5	9	4	6	1	7	2
1	7	4	5	2	3	9	6	8
2	9	6	7	8	1	5	3	4

SUDOKU #51

5	9	7	2	1	3	6	8	4
8	3	6	7	4	9	1	5	2
4	1	2	6	8	5	3	7	9
9	7	3	5	6	8	4	2	1
1	6	8	4	9	2	5	3	7
2	5	4	1	3	7	9	6	8
3	4	1	8	2	6	7	9	5
7	8	9	3	5	4	2	1	6
6	2	5	9	7	1	8	4	3

SUDOKU #52

7	1	5	2	8	9	6	4	3
6	9	3	4	1	5	8	7	2
8	4	2	7	3	6	9	5	1
4	2	7	3	5	8	1	9	6
5	8	9	1	6	7	3	2	4
1	3	6	9	2	4	5	8	7
2	5	8	6	7	3	4	1	9
9	6	1	8	4	2	7	3	5
3	7	4	5	9	1	2	6	8

SUDOKU #53

4	2	8	1	6	5	9	3	7
6	1	3	2	9	7	5	8	4
5	7	9	8	4	3	2	1	6
8	3	6	9	7	2	1	4	5
7	4	1	3	5	6	8	2	9
2	9	5	4	1	8	7	6	3
9	6	2	7	8	4	3	5	1
1	8	4	5	3	9	6	7	2
3	5	7	6	2	1	4	9	8

SUDOKU #54

4	1	2	9	7	3	5	8	6
7	8	6	5	2	1	3	9	4
3	9	5	4	6	8	1	7	2
9	7	4	2	3	5	6	1	8
8	2	3	6	1	7	9	4	5
5	6	1	8	9	4	2	3	7
2	4	9	1	8	6	7	5	3
1	5	7	3	4	2	8	6	9
6	3	8	7	5	9	4	2	1

SUDOKU #55

8	5	1	6	9	2	3	4	7
6	2	7	3	8	4	9	1	5
4	9	3	7	5	1	6	8	2
3	8	9	2	4	5	1	7	6
7	6	2	1	3	8	5	9	4
5	1	4	9	6	7	2	3	8
1	7	6	4	2	3	8	5	9
2	3	8	5	7	9	4	6	1
9	4	5	8	1	6	7	2	3

SUDOKU #56

3	5	6	7	9	1	8	2	4
8	9	4	2	6	3	7	5	1
1	2	7	4	5	8	3	9	6
5	4	3	1	8	2	9	6	7
7	6	1	3	4	9	5	8	2
9	8	2	5	7	6	4	1	3
6	7	5	8	2	4	1	3	9
4	1	9	6	3	5	2	7	8
2	3	8	9	1	7	6	4	5

SUDOKU #57

1	5	6	8	7	9	2	3	4
2	8	9	4	1	3	7	5	6
4	3	7	2	6	5	8	9	1
7	4	3	1	8	2	9	6	5
5	2	1	7	9	6	4	8	3
6	9	8	5	3	4	1	7	2
8	7	5	3	2	1	6	4	9
3	6	2	9	4	8	5	1	7
9	1	4	6	5	7	3	2	8

SUDOKU #58

7	6	9	3	5	2	4	1	8
3	4	2	8	1	6	7	9	5
5	1	8	9	7	4	6	3	2
6	7	3	5	4	1	2	8	9
9	2	4	7	3	8	5	6	1
1	8	5	2	6	9	3	4	7
2	5	1	6	9	3	8	7	4
4	3	7	1	8	5	9	2	6
8	9	6	4	2	7	1	5	3

SUDOKU #59

6	9	2	5	3	8	4	7	1
7	4	3	2	1	9	8	5	6
8	5	1	7	4	6	2	9	3
3	6	9	4	5	2	7	1	8
2	8	7	3	9	1	6	4	5
5	1	4	6	8	7	3	2	9
9	3	8	1	7	4	5	6	2
1	7	6	8	2	5	9	3	4
4	2	5	9	6	3	1	8	7

SUDOKU #60

2	9	6	1	7	5	8	4	3
7	4	8	3	9	6	2	1	5
5	1	3	8	2	4	6	7	9
6	3	4	2	5	7	9	8	1
9	7	2	4	8	1	5	3	6
8	5	1	9	6	3	4	2	7
1	8	7	5	4	9	3	6	2
4	6	5	7	3	2	1	9	8
3	2	9	6	1	8	7	5	4

SUDOKU #61

2	4	8	9	7	6	5	3	1
1	5	9	2	8	3	6	7	4
3	6	7	5	1	4	2	8	9
4	8	1	7	2	5	3	9	6
7	2	3	6	4	9	8	1	5
6	9	5	8	3	1	7	4	2
5	1	2	3	9	7	4	6	8
9	7	6	4	5	8	1	2	3
8	3	4	1	6	2	9	5	7

SUDOKU #62

6	5	3	7	4	2	9	8	1
4	9	8	6	1	5	3	7	2
1	7	2	8	3	9	4	6	5
8	6	9	4	2	3	5	1	7
7	2	1	5	9	8	6	3	4
3	4	5	1	7	6	8	2	9
5	3	7	9	8	1	2	4	6
2	1	6	3	5	4	7	9	8
9	8	4	2	6	7	1	5	3

SUDOKU #63

3	4	5	6	1	7	2	9	8
9	8	6	4	3	2	5	7	1
2	7	1	5	9	8	4	6	3
7	5	2	1	8	3	6	4	9
8	3	9	2	6	4	1	5	7
6	1	4	9	7	5	3	8	2
1	9	3	7	5	6	8	2	4
5	2	7	8	4	1	9	3	6
4	6	8	3	2	9	7	1	5

SUDOKU #64

6	1	3	7	5	4	8	2	9
5	8	7	9	3	2	6	4	1
2	4	9	1	8	6	3	7	5
4	9	6	8	7	5	2	1	3
1	2	8	3	4	9	5	6	7
3	7	5	2	6	1	4	9	8
9	5	1	4	2	8	7	3	6
7	6	4	5	1	3	9	8	2
8	3	2	6	9	7	1	5	4

SUDOKU #65

6	3	9	1	5	2	7	8	4
8	7	2	9	4	6	3	5	1
4	1	5	8	3	7	9	2	6
3	5	1	6	8	9	4	7	2
2	9	4	7	1	5	6	3	8
7	8	6	3	2	4	1	9	5
1	2	7	4	9	8	5	6	3
5	6	3	2	7	1	8	4	9
9	4	8	5	6	3	2	1	7

SUDOKU #66

2	5	8	1	7	9	4	3	6
7	9	3	8	6	4	5	1	2
4	1	6	2	3	5	7	8	9
6	7	5	9	1	3	2	4	8
3	2	4	5	8	7	9	6	1
9	8	1	4	2	6	3	7	5
1	3	7	6	9	2	8	5	4
5	6	9	7	4	8	1	2	3
8	4	2	3	5	1	6	9	7

SUDOKU #67

8	3	9	1	5	4	2	6	7
5	7	4	2	8	6	9	3	1
1	2	6	3	9	7	4	8	5
9	6	3	4	7	1	5	2	8
2	4	8	5	3	9	7	1	6
7	5	1	6	2	8	3	9	4
4	9	5	8	6	3	1	7	2
6	1	7	9	4	2	8	5	3
3	8	2	7	1	5	6	4	9

SUDOKU #68

6	5	9	4	1	8	7	2	3
1	8	4	3	7	2	6	5	9
3	7	2	9	6	5	8	4	1
5	3	7	1	9	4	2	6	8
8	2	1	7	5	6	9	3	4
9	4	6	2	8	3	5	1	7
7	1	3	5	2	9	4	8	6
4	6	5	8	3	7	1	9	2
2	9	8	6	4	1	3	7	5

SUDOKU #69

6	1	4	3	5	2	8	7	9
5	8	7	9	4	1	3	2	6
2	3	9	7	6	8	4	1	5
9	4	8	2	3	7	5	6	1
1	2	5	6	8	9	7	4	3
3	7	6	5	1	4	2	9	8
8	6	2	1	7	5	9	3	4
7	5	3	4	9	6	1	8	2
4	9	1	8	2	3	6	5	7

SUDOKU #70

5	6	7	4	1	8	3	9	2
3	2	4	6	9	5	7	1	8
9	1	8	3	2	7	6	4	5
7	3	9	2	5	1	4	8	6
6	4	1	7	8	3	5	2	9
2	8	5	9	6	4	1	3	7
1	9	6	5	3	2	8	7	4
8	7	2	1	4	6	9	5	3
4	5	3	8	7	9	2	6	1

SUDOKU #71

7	9	8	4	5	1	3	2	6
3	2	4	9	7	6	5	1	8
6	1	5	2	8	3	9	4	7
8	5	9	6	3	2	4	7	1
1	4	6	7	9	8	2	3	5
2	3	7	5	1	4	6	8	9
9	6	2	1	4	7	8	5	3
5	8	1	3	2	9	7	6	4
4	7	3	8	6	5	1	9	2

SUDOKU #72

7	2	1	5	8	9	3	4	6
4	3	9	6	1	7	8	2	5
6	5	8	2	3	4	9	1	7
8	9	7	4	6	2	5	3	1
5	1	2	3	7	8	6	9	4
3	4	6	9	5	1	7	8	2
2	6	3	8	4	5	1	7	9
9	7	5	1	2	3	4	6	8
1	8	4	7	9	6	2	5	3

SUDOKU #73

2	4	1	6	8	5	3	9	7
6	3	5	7	9	1	8	2	4
7	9	8	4	2	3	1	6	5
3	8	6	2	5	9	7	4	1
5	7	4	1	6	8	2	3	9
9	1	2	3	4	7	6	5	8
8	5	7	9	3	2	4	1	6
1	6	3	5	7	4	9	8	2
4	2	9	8	1	6	5	7	3

SUDOKU #74

7	5	1	2	4	6	9	8	3
4	6	8	9	7	3	1	2	5
3	2	9	5	8	1	4	6	7
8	4	6	3	1	9	5	7	2
5	1	3	8	2	7	6	4	9
2	9	7	6	5	4	3	1	8
9	8	4	7	6	5	2	3	1
6	3	2	1	9	8	7	5	4
1	7	5	4	3	2	8	9	6

SUDOKU #75

5	9	8	2	1	7	6	3	4
7	6	2	9	4	3	1	8	5
3	1	4	8	5	6	9	2	7
8	4	6	1	7	9	3	5	2
1	7	9	3	2	5	8	4	6
2	5	3	6	8	4	7	9	1
9	2	7	4	6	8	5	1	3
6	3	1	5	9	2	4	7	8
4	8	5	7	3	1	2	6	9

SUDOKU #76

7	1	9	4	8	5	6	3	2
5	6	3	1	9	2	4	7	8
4	2	8	3	7	6	5	1	9
9	4	6	5	3	7	8	2	1
8	5	7	2	1	9	3	6	4
1	3	2	8	6	4	7	9	5
2	7	5	6	4	1	9	8	3
3	9	4	7	2	8	1	5	6
6	8	1	9	5	3	2	4	7

SUDOKU #77

7	3	6	4	8	2	9	5	1
5	8	2	9	7	1	3	4	6
1	9	4	5	6	3	7	2	8
9	4	7	8	1	5	2	6	3
2	5	1	3	4	6	8	9	7
8	6	3	2	9	7	5	1	4
4	2	8	6	3	9	1	7	5
3	7	5	1	2	4	6	8	9
6	1	9	7	5	8	4	3	2

SUDOKU #78

4	2	9	3	1	7	5	8	6
7	3	6	5	4	8	2	1	9
1	5	8	9	2	6	4	3	7
9	4	5	7	8	1	6	2	3
6	8	7	2	9	3	1	4	5
2	1	3	4	6	5	7	9	8
3	9	1	6	5	4	8	7	2
8	6	2	1	7	9	3	5	4
5	7	4	8	3	2	9	6	1

SUDOKU #79

4	2	6	8	5	7	9	3	1
3	7	1	6	9	4	8	2	5
5	9	8	3	1	2	4	6	7
7	5	2	9	4	6	1	8	3
8	6	9	5	3	1	7	4	2
1	3	4	2	7	8	5	9	6
9	1	3	4	6	5	2	7	8
6	8	5	7	2	9	3	1	4
2	4	7	1	8	3	6	5	9

SUDOKU #80

8	2	6	4	5	9	3	7	1
1	4	7	8	3	2	9	6	5
5	3	9	7	1	6	2	8	4
6	9	8	1	2	4	7	5	3
4	5	3	9	6	7	1	2	8
7	1	2	5	8	3	4	9	6
2	6	4	3	9	8	5	1	7
9	7	1	6	4	5	8	3	2
3	8	5	2	7	1	6	4	9

SUDOKU #81

1	6	8	2	9	3	5	7	4
4	9	3	7	5	8	6	2	1
2	7	5	6	1	4	9	8	3
6	3	1	4	8	2	7	5	9
5	4	2	9	7	6	3	1	8
7	8	9	1	3	5	2	4	6
8	5	6	3	2	1	4	9	7
3	2	7	8	4	9	1	6	5
9	1	4	5	6	7	8	3	2

SUDOKU #82

4	2	3	7	6	5	1	8	9
5	9	7	3	8	1	6	2	4
1	8	6	2	4	9	7	3	5
9	4	2	6	5	8	3	1	7
3	6	8	4	1	7	9	5	2
7	1	5	9	3	2	4	6	8
8	5	4	1	9	3	2	7	6
2	3	9	5	7	6	8	4	1
6	7	1	8	2	4	5	9	3

SUDOKU #83

5	2	8	7	9	3	6	4	1
4	7	6	5	2	1	9	3	8
1	9	3	8	4	6	5	7	2
9	6	2	4	1	8	7	5	3
7	3	1	2	6	5	4	8	9
8	4	5	9	3	7	2	1	6
2	5	9	1	8	4	3	6	7
3	8	4	6	7	2	1	9	5
6	1	7	3	5	9	8	2	4

SUDOKU #84

3	7	2	6	5	1	9	4	8
9	5	6	8	3	4	2	1	7
8	1	4	9	7	2	3	5	6
6	2	3	4	1	8	5	7	9
5	8	7	2	9	3	4	6	1
1	4	9	7	6	5	8	3	2
4	9	5	1	8	6	7	2	3
2	6	8	3	4	7	1	9	5
7	3	1	5	2	9	6	8	4

SUDOKU #85

2	9	8	5	1	7	6	3	4
3	4	6	9	8	2	1	7	5
1	7	5	3	4	6	9	8	2
9	6	4	7	3	8	5	2	1
8	3	1	2	6	5	4	9	7
7	5	2	4	9	1	3	6	8
4	2	9	8	5	3	7	1	6
6	8	3	1	7	4	2	5	9
5	1	7	6	2	9	8	4	3

SUDOKU #86

2	7	9	5	4	8	1	6	3
3	6	1	7	9	2	5	4	8
8	5	4	1	3	6	9	2	7
5	1	6	2	8	3	7	9	4
7	8	2	9	5	4	6	3	1
9	4	3	6	1	7	2	8	5
4	9	7	8	2	5	3	1	6
6	2	8	3	7	1	4	5	9
1	3	5	4	6	9	8	7	2

SUDOKU #87

7	9	6	8	4	1	5	2	3
8	3	4	5	7	2	9	6	1
5	1	2	9	6	3	4	8	7
9	4	8	6	3	5	1	7	2
3	6	7	2	1	4	8	5	9
1	2	5	7	8	9	6	3	4
6	5	3	1	9	7	2	4	8
2	7	9	4	5	8	3	1	6
4	8	1	3	2	6	7	9	5

SUDOKU #88

1	6	5	3	8	2	7	4	9
2	3	9	6	4	7	8	1	5
4	8	7	5	1	9	2	3	6
6	1	4	7	9	8	5	2	3
8	9	2	1	3	5	6	7	4
7	5	3	4	2	6	9	8	1
9	2	1	8	6	4	3	5	7
3	7	6	2	5	1	4	9	8
5	4	8	9	7	3	1	6	2

SUDOKU #89

9	4	5	7	2	6	3	8	1
3	2	8	1	5	4	6	7	9
6	1	7	3	8	9	2	4	5
2	9	3	8	6	5	7	1	4
7	5	4	9	1	3	8	6	2
1	8	6	2	4	7	9	5	3
4	3	1	6	7	2	5	9	8
8	7	2	5	9	1	4	3	6
5	6	9	4	3	8	1	2	7

SUDOKU #90

5	7	8	1	4	3	6	9	2
4	9	3	7	2	6	1	5	8
1	6	2	9	5	8	4	3	7
9	2	4	3	7	1	5	8	6
7	3	6	5	8	2	9	1	4
8	1	5	6	9	4	2	7	3
2	4	7	8	1	5	3	6	9
6	8	1	4	3	9	7	2	5
3	5	9	2	6	7	8	4	1

SUDOKU #91

3	9	2	8	1	6	4	7	5
6	4	8	2	5	7	9	1	3
5	7	1	9	3	4	6	2	8
2	1	9	4	6	5	3	8	7
4	8	5	7	2	3	1	6	9
7	6	3	1	8	9	5	4	2
8	3	7	6	9	1	2	5	4
1	5	4	3	7	2	8	9	6
9	2	6	5	4	8	7	3	1

SUDOKU #92

6	9	3	1	4	2	8	7	5
7	2	4	5	8	9	3	6	1
1	8	5	7	3	6	4	2	9
9	1	2	3	7	8	6	5	4
3	6	7	9	5	4	1	8	2
4	5	8	2	6	1	9	3	7
8	7	6	4	1	5	2	9	3
5	4	9	8	2	3	7	1	6
2	3	1	6	9	7	5	4	8

SUDOKU #93

3	6	1	9	5	4	2	8	7
9	2	4	7	6	8	5	3	1
5	7	8	3	1	2	6	9	4
8	4	7	5	2	3	1	6	9
2	1	3	6	9	7	4	5	8
6	9	5	4	8	1	3	7	2
7	8	2	1	3	6	9	4	5
4	3	9	2	7	5	8	1	6
1	5	6	8	4	9	7	2	3

SUDOKU #94

2	7	6	8	1	3	9	4	5
3	5	1	4	9	2	6	7	8
4	8	9	5	7	6	1	2	3
5	4	2	1	8	7	3	6	9
1	3	7	6	4	9	5	8	2
9	6	8	3	2	5	4	1	7
7	2	3	9	6	4	8	5	1
8	9	4	7	5	1	2	3	6
6	1	5	2	3	8	7	9	4

SUDOKU #95

4	3	9	1	2	5	8	6	7
5	2	8	6	3	7	4	9	1
6	7	1	8	9	4	3	2	5
1	6	2	7	8	3	9	5	4
7	9	5	4	1	6	2	3	8
3	8	4	2	5	9	1	7	6
8	5	6	9	4	2	7	1	3
2	1	7	3	6	8	5	4	9
9	4	3	5	7	1	6	8	2

SUDOKU #96

6	7	4	5	2	8	9	3	1
2	3	8	6	1	9	5	4	7
5	1	9	7	4	3	2	8	6
7	5	1	2	9	4	3	6	8
8	6	2	1	3	5	7	9	4
4	9	3	8	6	7	1	2	5
1	4	6	9	5	2	8	7	3
9	8	5	3	7	6	4	1	2
3	2	7	4	8	1	6	5	9

SUDOKU #97

6	2	1	9	4	7	5	8	3
3	8	4	2	5	6	9	7	1
9	7	5	8	3	1	4	6	2
1	6	8	7	2	5	3	9	4
5	4	9	6	1	3	7	2	8
2	3	7	4	9	8	1	5	6
7	1	2	3	6	9	8	4	5
4	9	3	5	8	2	6	1	7
8	5	6	1	7	4	2	3	9

SUDOKU #98

2	5	1	6	8	7	9	3	4
8	4	7	9	3	2	6	1	5
3	9	6	5	1	4	7	8	2
9	2	3	4	5	1	8	7	6
5	1	8	2	7	6	3	4	9
6	7	4	8	9	3	2	5	1
1	6	2	3	4	8	5	9	7
4	3	9	7	2	5	1	6	8
7	8	5	1	6	9	4	2	3

SUDOKU #99

7	4	1	8	2	3	6	5	9
5	8	2	1	9	6	3	4	7
6	3	9	7	4	5	8	2	1
3	7	5	4	6	1	2	9	8
9	1	8	2	3	7	4	6	5
4	2	6	5	8	9	7	1	3
1	6	7	3	5	2	9	8	4
8	9	3	6	1	4	5	7	2
2	5	4	9	7	8	1	3	6

SUDOKU #100

9	2	7	6	4	1	8	5	3
8	1	5	3	7	9	2	6	4
3	6	4	8	5	2	1	7	9
7	5	2	1	8	4	3	9	6
1	4	3	7	9	6	5	8	2
6	8	9	2	3	5	4	1	7
5	3	1	4	6	7	9	2	8
4	9	6	5	2	8	7	3	1
2	7	8	9	1	3	6	4	5

SUDOKU #101

8	2	7	3	5	4	9	6	1
3	4	9	6	1	8	5	7	2
5	6	1	2	7	9	8	3	4
1	9	2	8	6	5	7	4	3
6	3	5	4	2	7	1	8	9
7	8	4	1	9	3	2	5	6
2	1	8	7	3	6	4	9	5
4	5	6	9	8	1	3	2	7
9	7	3	5	4	2	6	1	8

SUDOKU #102

9	8	6	4	1	5	3	2	7
1	4	7	3	9	2	8	6	5
3	2	5	8	6	7	9	1	4
7	3	4	9	2	8	1	5	6
2	6	9	5	3	1	4	7	8
8	5	1	7	4	6	2	9	3
5	7	3	1	8	9	6	4	2
6	9	8	2	5	4	7	3	1
4	1	2	6	7	3	5	8	9

SUDOKU #103

9	7	5	4	3	8	1	6	2
4	2	6	1	5	7	3	8	9
8	1	3	6	2	9	7	5	4
5	6	9	7	8	2	4	3	1
1	4	8	9	6	3	2	7	5
2	3	7	5	1	4	8	9	6
7	5	2	8	4	6	9	1	3
3	9	1	2	7	5	6	4	8
6	8	4	3	9	1	5	2	7

SUDOKU #104

9	4	1	6	2	3	5	8	7
3	2	5	8	1	7	6	9	4
7	8	6	5	4	9	1	3	2
8	6	9	3	7	1	4	2	5
5	1	7	4	8	2	9	6	3
4	3	2	9	6	5	7	1	8
1	5	8	2	9	4	3	7	6
2	9	3	7	5	6	8	4	1
6	7	4	1	3	8	2	5	9

SUDOKU #105

9	8	1	3	5	4	7	2	6
7	4	6	1	9	2	5	8	3
5	2	3	7	6	8	4	1	9
6	1	2	4	8	5	3	9	7
8	3	9	6	1	7	2	5	4
4	5	7	9	2	3	8	6	1
2	6	4	5	3	9	1	7	8
1	7	8	2	4	6	9	3	5
3	9	5	8	7	1	6	4	2

SUDOKU #106

8	9	1	3	5	6	2	4	7
3	5	2	9	4	7	8	6	1
6	4	7	8	1	2	3	9	5
9	7	6	4	3	8	5	1	2
2	1	5	6	7	9	4	3	8
4	3	8	5	2	1	6	7	9
5	2	9	7	6	4	1	8	3
7	6	3	1	8	5	9	2	4
1	8	4	2	9	3	7	5	6

SUDOKU #107

8	4	2	3	5	1	9	6	7
9	3	6	7	8	2	5	1	4
5	7	1	9	6	4	8	2	3
3	9	8	6	1	5	7	4	2
4	1	7	8	2	9	6	3	5
6	2	5	4	7	3	1	8	9
1	6	3	5	4	7	2	9	8
2	5	4	1	9	8	3	7	6
7	8	9	2	3	6	4	5	1

SUDOKU #108

3	1	7	2	5	4	6	9	8
4	9	8	7	6	3	1	2	5
2	5	6	9	8	1	3	4	7
9	4	2	8	3	6	5	7	1
8	3	1	5	7	2	4	6	9
7	6	5	1	4	9	8	3	2
5	7	3	4	9	8	2	1	6
6	2	9	3	1	5	7	8	4
1	8	4	6	2	7	9	5	3

SUDOKU #109

8	2	4	3	1	6	5	9	7
6	7	3	5	2	9	8	1	4
5	9	1	7	8	4	6	3	2
7	8	5	4	3	1	9	2	6
2	3	9	6	5	7	4	8	1
4	1	6	8	9	2	7	5	3
3	4	2	9	6	5	1	7	8
1	5	7	2	4	8	3	6	9
9	6	8	1	7	3	2	4	5

SUDOKU #110

9	1	4	5	3	8	6	2	7
6	7	5	1	4	2	3	8	9
8	3	2	9	6	7	5	4	1
5	9	6	3	7	4	2	1	8
7	8	1	2	5	6	4	9	3
4	2	3	8	1	9	7	6	5
3	6	8	4	9	5	1	7	2
2	5	7	6	8	1	9	3	4
1	4	9	7	2	3	8	5	6

SUDOKU #111

1	6	5	8	7	3	9	4	2
3	7	4	2	6	9	1	5	8
2	9	8	5	1	4	7	6	3
7	1	9	4	3	2	5	8	6
8	5	2	1	9	6	3	7	4
4	3	6	7	8	5	2	1	9
6	4	3	9	5	1	8	2	7
9	8	1	6	2	7	4	3	5
5	2	7	3	4	8	6	9	1

SUDOKU #112

7	4	3	2	1	6	5	8	9
8	5	1	4	7	9	3	2	6
9	6	2	3	8	5	7	4	1
5	8	4	9	3	2	6	1	7
2	7	9	8	6	1	4	3	5
1	3	6	7	5	4	8	9	2
3	1	7	5	2	8	9	6	4
4	2	5	6	9	3	1	7	8
6	9	8	1	4	7	2	5	3

SUDOKU #113

6	8	2	3	1	7	5	9	4
9	4	1	5	2	6	3	7	8
3	7	5	4	8	9	2	6	1
8	3	6	1	9	5	7	4	2
2	1	4	8	7	3	6	5	9
7	5	9	2	6	4	8	1	3
5	6	8	9	3	1	4	2	7
4	9	3	7	5	2	1	8	6
1	2	7	6	4	8	9	3	5

SUDOKU #114

1	9	8	2	4	5	6	7	3
6	4	3	7	8	1	9	5	2
5	7	2	6	3	9	8	4	1
4	3	9	5	6	8	2	1	7
8	5	7	4	1	2	3	9	6
2	1	6	9	7	3	4	8	5
9	6	1	8	2	7	5	3	4
3	2	5	1	9	4	7	6	8
7	8	4	3	5	6	1	2	9

SUDOKU #115

4	7	3	1	8	6	9	2	5
2	1	8	5	3	9	6	7	4
6	5	9	4	2	7	1	8	3
9	8	4	3	1	2	5	6	7
5	3	6	8	7	4	2	1	9
7	2	1	6	9	5	3	4	8
3	9	2	7	6	8	4	5	1
1	4	7	2	5	3	8	9	6
8	6	5	9	4	1	7	3	2

SUDOKU #116

1	4	6	3	9	2	5	7	8
3	9	5	4	7	8	6	2	1
8	2	7	6	5	1	4	9	3
2	7	9	5	8	4	1	3	6
6	5	1	7	2	3	9	8	4
4	8	3	9	1	6	7	5	2
7	1	8	2	4	9	3	6	5
5	6	4	8	3	7	2	1	9
9	3	2	1	6	5	8	4	7

SUDOKU #117

8	3	2	5	6	4	1	9	7
6	9	4	7	1	3	5	8	2
5	1	7	8	2	9	4	3	6
2	8	3	6	9	5	7	4	1
9	4	5	1	3	7	2	6	8
1	7	6	2	4	8	9	5	3
3	5	8	9	7	2	6	1	4
4	2	1	3	5	6	8	7	9
7	6	9	4	8	1	3	2	5

SUDOKU #118

7	5	4	6	3	9	1	2	8
9	1	2	4	8	7	5	3	6
6	3	8	5	2	1	4	9	7
3	2	5	8	6	4	9	7	1
8	6	7	1	9	3	2	4	5
1	4	9	2	7	5	6	8	3
5	8	1	3	4	2	7	6	9
4	7	6	9	1	8	3	5	2
2	9	3	7	5	6	8	1	4

SUDOKU #119

6	1	5	3	2	7	4	8	9
9	3	8	6	4	1	7	2	5
4	2	7	9	8	5	1	6	3
2	8	3	4	5	6	9	1	7
5	6	1	8	7	9	3	4	2
7	9	4	2	1	3	8	5	6
3	4	9	1	6	2	5	7	8
1	7	2	5	9	8	6	3	4
8	5	6	7	3	4	2	9	1

SUDOKU #120

2	4	7	3	8	1	6	9	5
5	6	9	7	2	4	8	1	3
3	1	8	5	6	9	2	7	4
7	2	4	9	5	6	3	8	1
6	3	5	8	1	2	9	4	7
9	8	1	4	7	3	5	6	2
1	5	2	6	4	8	7	3	9
4	9	6	2	3	7	1	5	8
8	7	3	1	9	5	4	2	6

SUDOKU #121

7	3	8	6	2	1	9	5	4
2	4	9	5	7	3	6	1	8
1	5	6	4	8	9	2	3	7
4	7	2	9	6	5	3	8	1
3	6	5	8	1	2	7	4	9
8	9	1	7	3	4	5	2	6
6	2	3	1	9	8	4	7	5
9	1	4	3	5	7	8	6	2
5	8	7	2	4	6	1	9	3

SUDOKU #122

3	7	8	5	4	6	1	9	2
2	9	6	3	1	8	7	5	4
1	5	4	7	2	9	8	6	3
6	1	3	2	5	7	9	4	8
4	2	9	6	8	3	5	7	1
7	8	5	4	9	1	3	2	6
9	6	1	8	7	2	4	3	5
8	4	2	9	3	5	6	1	7
5	3	7	1	6	4	2	8	9

SUDOKU #123

6	4	2	1	5	7	8	9	3
8	5	1	3	6	9	7	2	4
3	7	9	4	8	2	6	1	5
1	3	4	2	7	5	9	6	8
2	9	7	6	4	8	3	5	1
5	6	8	9	1	3	4	7	2
4	2	5	8	9	6	1	3	7
7	8	6	5	3	1	2	4	9
9	1	3	7	2	4	5	8	6

SUDOKU #124

7	4	1	5	8	6	9	3	2
6	3	5	9	1	2	4	8	7
8	9	2	4	3	7	6	5	1
2	5	9	6	7	8	3	1	4
3	7	8	1	9	4	2	6	5
1	6	4	2	5	3	7	9	8
5	8	3	7	2	9	1	4	6
9	2	6	8	4	1	5	7	3
4	1	7	3	6	5	8	2	9

SUDOKU #125

8	2	7	1	9	4	6	5	3
3	1	4	6	5	7	2	8	9
9	5	6	3	2	8	4	1	7
1	7	8	4	6	3	9	2	5
6	4	2	9	1	5	3	7	8
5	3	9	7	8	2	1	4	6
4	9	3	8	7	1	5	6	2
2	8	1	5	3	6	7	9	4
7	6	5	2	4	9	8	3	1

SUDOKU #126

4	7	2	8	5	1	6	9	3
5	3	6	4	9	2	8	7	1
1	9	8	6	3	7	5	2	4
9	5	4	3	8	6	2	1	7
3	6	1	7	2	9	4	5	8
2	8	7	1	4	5	9	3	6
6	1	5	9	7	8	3	4	2
8	2	3	5	1	4	7	6	9
7	4	9	2	6	3	1	8	5

SUDOKU #127

9	4	3	2	8	5	7	6	1
7	1	5	9	6	3	2	8	4
2	8	6	7	1	4	3	9	5
5	6	4	3	7	9	8	1	2
3	9	8	6	2	1	5	4	7
1	2	7	4	5	8	6	3	9
4	7	2	8	9	6	1	5	3
8	5	9	1	3	7	4	2	6
6	3	1	5	4	2	9	7	8

SUDOKU #128

6	3	1	4	8	5	9	7	2
7	4	8	9	6	2	1	5	3
9	2	5	3	1	7	8	6	4
8	5	9	7	2	1	3	4	6
2	1	3	5	4	6	7	8	9
4	6	7	8	3	9	2	1	5
3	8	2	1	5	4	6	9	7
5	7	6	2	9	8	4	3	1
1	9	4	6	7	3	5	2	8

SUDOKU #129

4	8	5	7	2	6	3	1	9
9	6	2	1	8	3	5	7	4
1	7	3	4	5	9	6	8	2
7	4	1	5	6	2	8	9	3
3	5	8	9	1	4	7	2	6
6	2	9	3	7	8	4	5	1
2	1	4	8	3	5	9	6	7
8	3	6	2	9	7	1	4	5
5	9	7	6	4	1	2	3	8

SUDOKU #130

6	7	9	2	8	5	3	1	4
1	3	4	6	9	7	2	8	5
8	2	5	1	3	4	6	9	7
4	8	6	5	2	9	7	3	1
7	1	3	4	6	8	9	5	2
9	5	2	3	7	1	4	6	8
3	6	1	7	5	2	8	4	9
2	4	8	9	1	3	5	7	6
5	9	7	8	4	6	1	2	3

SUDOKU #131

3	1	6	2	7	5	8	9	4
7	2	9	4	3	8	6	5	1
5	4	8	6	9	1	3	2	7
6	7	2	9	1	4	5	8	3
1	9	3	8	5	6	4	7	2
4	8	5	7	2	3	9	1	6
8	6	7	1	4	9	2	3	5
9	5	1	3	6	2	7	4	8
2	3	4	5	8	7	1	6	9

SUDOKU #132

8	1	5	3	9	6	2	4	7
4	6	7	2	1	5	9	3	8
3	2	9	4	8	7	1	6	5
5	8	3	7	2	1	6	9	4
6	9	4	8	5	3	7	1	2
2	7	1	9	6	4	8	5	3
9	4	6	5	7	8	3	2	1
1	3	8	6	4	2	5	7	9
7	5	2	1	3	9	4	8	6

SUDOKU #133

1	9	7	6	2	5	4	8	3
6	8	2	3	4	9	5	7	1
5	3	4	7	1	8	6	9	2
2	1	9	5	7	6	8	3	4
8	4	3	1	9	2	7	5	6
7	5	6	4	8	3	2	1	9
3	2	1	8	5	4	9	6	7
4	7	8	9	6	1	3	2	5
9	6	5	2	3	7	1	4	8

SUDOKU #134

2	3	5	4	1	6	7	8	9
7	6	4	9	8	2	3	5	1
1	9	8	3	5	7	4	6	2
8	4	6	1	3	9	5	2	7
5	2	3	8	7	4	1	9	6
9	7	1	6	2	5	8	4	3
6	1	9	7	4	8	2	3	5
3	8	2	5	6	1	9	7	4
4	5	7	2	9	3	6	1	8

SUDOKU #135

8	6	9	4	5	1	3	7	2
1	2	4	7	6	3	8	5	9
7	5	3	9	8	2	4	1	6
5	9	7	3	4	6	2	8	1
2	4	8	1	9	5	7	6	3
3	1	6	2	7	8	5	9	4
9	7	1	5	3	4	6	2	8
4	8	2	6	1	7	9	3	5
6	3	5	8	2	9	1	4	7

SUDOKU #136

6	3	4	1	2	5	7	9	8
8	7	2	3	4	9	5	1	6
9	5	1	8	6	7	4	2	3
2	6	3	7	1	4	8	5	9
5	4	7	6	9	8	2	3	1
1	9	8	2	5	3	6	7	4
3	8	5	9	7	6	1	4	2
7	1	9	4	8	2	3	6	5
4	2	6	5	3	1	9	8	7

SUDOKU #137

5	1	2	6	8	7	4	3	9
8	4	6	2	9	3	7	5	1
9	3	7	5	4	1	8	6	2
3	5	8	1	2	6	9	4	7
1	7	4	9	3	8	5	2	6
2	6	9	4	7	5	3	1	8
6	8	5	7	1	4	2	9	3
7	2	1	3	5	9	6	8	4
4	9	3	8	6	2	1	7	5

SUDOKU #138

8	9	6	1	4	7	3	5	2
3	5	1	2	6	8	4	9	7
2	7	4	5	9	3	6	8	1
7	1	8	6	5	4	9	2	3
9	6	3	7	1	2	8	4	5
4	2	5	3	8	9	7	1	6
6	8	7	9	2	5	1	3	4
1	4	2	8	3	6	5	7	9
5	3	9	4	7	1	2	6	8

SUDOKU #139

8	2	1	6	9	3	5	4	7
3	5	4	1	7	8	9	6	2
9	7	6	4	5	2	1	3	8
7	1	9	2	6	5	4	8	3
2	6	3	8	4	9	7	5	1
5	4	8	7	3	1	6	2	9
1	3	5	9	2	4	8	7	6
4	9	7	3	8	6	2	1	5
6	8	2	5	1	7	3	9	4

SUDOKU #140

9	8	7	2	4	6	5	3	1
2	5	3	8	7	1	4	6	9
4	6	1	5	9	3	7	8	2
3	1	9	7	8	5	6	2	4
7	4	8	6	1	2	9	5	3
5	2	6	4	3	9	1	7	8
8	3	5	9	6	4	2	1	7
6	7	4	1	2	8	3	9	5
1	9	2	3	5	7	8	4	6

SUDOKU #141

9	5	7	2	4	6	3	8	1
8	6	1	5	3	9	7	2	4
2	4	3	7	8	1	5	6	9
1	2	9	3	7	5	8	4	6
5	3	4	6	1	8	9	7	2
6	7	8	9	2	4	1	3	5
4	9	2	8	5	7	6	1	3
7	1	5	4	6	3	2	9	8
3	8	6	1	9	2	4	5	7

SUDOKU #142

4	6	5	3	8	7	9	2	1
7	3	9	2	1	4	6	8	5
2	1	8	6	9	5	4	7	3
6	5	2	8	4	3	7	1	9
9	7	4	5	6	1	2	3	8
1	8	3	9	7	2	5	4	6
8	4	6	1	2	9	3	5	7
3	9	7	4	5	8	1	6	2
5	2	1	7	3	6	8	9	4

SUDOKU #143

6	4	7	2	5	1	9	3	8
3	8	5	9	4	6	2	1	7
1	9	2	8	7	3	6	5	4
4	7	9	6	3	8	5	2	1
5	2	6	4	1	9	7	8	3
8	1	3	7	2	5	4	9	6
2	5	8	3	6	7	1	4	9
7	3	4	1	9	2	8	6	5
9	6	1	5	8	4	3	7	2

SUDOKU #144

3	1	5	9	7	6	2	8	4
6	8	7	2	4	1	9	3	5
4	2	9	3	8	5	6	7	1
7	9	1	8	6	4	5	2	3
5	6	4	7	2	3	1	9	8
2	3	8	5	1	9	7	4	6
9	7	6	1	3	8	4	5	2
1	5	3	4	9	2	8	6	7
8	4	2	6	5	7	3	1	9

SUDOKU #145

9	7	5	3	1	2	6	8	4
2	6	8	9	4	5	1	3	7
1	3	4	7	8	6	5	9	2
4	5	3	1	9	7	8	2	6
6	1	9	4	2	8	7	5	3
7	8	2	6	5	3	4	1	9
8	4	1	2	7	9	3	6	5
5	9	6	8	3	4	2	7	1
3	2	7	5	6	1	9	4	8

SUDOKU #146

1	2	7	8	3	9	6	5	4
5	8	3	7	6	4	9	2	1
9	6	4	5	2	1	3	8	7
3	4	1	6	9	2	8	7	5
6	5	2	4	8	7	1	3	9
7	9	8	1	5	3	2	4	6
2	3	6	9	7	5	4	1	8
8	1	5	2	4	6	7	9	3
4	7	9	3	1	8	5	6	2

SUDOKU #147

1	6	2	4	8	3	7	9	5
8	7	4	5	6	9	1	2	3
9	5	3	1	7	2	8	6	4
5	3	1	9	4	7	6	8	2
6	9	8	3	2	5	4	1	7
2	4	7	8	1	6	5	3	9
7	8	6	2	3	4	9	5	1
4	2	9	6	5	1	3	7	8
3	1	5	7	9	8	2	4	6

SUDOKU #148

1	4	7	3	2	5	9	6	8
2	6	8	7	4	9	1	3	5
3	9	5	8	1	6	7	2	4
4	7	3	1	6	2	5	8	9
8	1	2	9	5	7	6	4	3
9	5	6	4	3	8	2	1	7
5	8	1	2	7	3	4	9	6
6	3	4	5	9	1	8	7	2
7	2	9	6	8	4	3	5	1

SUDOKU #149

8	3	6	5	1	4	9	2	7
4	1	7	2	9	8	3	5	6
2	9	5	3	7	6	1	4	8
1	5	3	7	6	9	4	8	2
7	6	2	4	8	3	5	1	9
9	4	8	1	5	2	7	6	3
5	8	9	6	4	7	2	3	1
3	7	1	8	2	5	6	9	4
6	2	4	9	3	1	8	7	5

SUDOKU #150

7	2	3	5	1	4	8	9	6
5	4	9	8	6	3	2	7	1
6	8	1	7	2	9	4	5	3
2	1	4	6	3	5	9	8	7
9	6	5	1	7	8	3	2	4
3	7	8	4	9	2	6	1	5
1	9	7	2	4	6	5	3	8
8	3	6	9	5	7	1	4	2
4	5	2	3	8	1	7	6	9

SUDOKU #151

1	3	7	4	6	9	8	5	2
5	8	9	2	3	7	1	6	4
2	6	4	5	8	1	7	3	9
6	7	2	8	9	3	5	4	1
3	5	1	6	2	4	9	7	8
9	4	8	7	1	5	3	2	6
7	2	5	1	4	8	6	9	3
4	1	3	9	7	6	2	8	5
8	9	6	3	5	2	4	1	7

SUDOKU #152

4	1	2	7	8	3	5	9	6
7	8	5	6	2	9	3	1	4
9	6	3	5	4	1	2	7	8
6	3	7	8	9	2	1	4	5
5	9	1	4	6	7	8	2	3
2	4	8	1	3	5	9	6	7
8	5	9	2	7	4	6	3	1
1	2	4	3	5	6	7	8	9
3	7	6	9	1	8	4	5	2

SUDOKU #153

5	1	2	9	7	3	4	8	6
8	6	7	2	1	4	9	3	5
9	4	3	8	5	6	2	1	7
4	9	5	1	3	8	7	6	2
1	3	6	7	4	2	5	9	8
2	7	8	5	6	9	1	4	3
3	2	1	6	9	7	8	5	4
6	8	9	4	2	5	3	7	1
7	5	4	3	8	1	6	2	9

SUDOKU #154

4	8	6	9	5	3	2	7	1
5	3	2	1	4	7	6	8	9
9	1	7	8	6	2	4	5	3
7	9	1	2	8	4	5	3	6
8	5	3	7	9	6	1	4	2
2	6	4	3	1	5	8	9	7
1	2	8	4	3	9	7	6	5
3	7	5	6	2	8	9	1	4
6	4	9	5	7	1	3	2	8

SUDOKU #155

1	5	3	2	7	9	8	6	4
2	8	9	3	6	4	5	7	1
7	6	4	1	5	8	3	2	9
5	9	2	6	1	3	7	4	8
6	3	7	4	8	5	9	1	2
8	4	1	7	9	2	6	5	3
9	1	8	5	2	7	4	3	6
3	7	6	9	4	1	2	8	5
4	2	5	8	3	6	1	9	7

SUDOKU #156

3	4	2	6	5	8	1	7	9
5	6	7	1	9	3	8	2	4
8	9	1	2	4	7	3	5	6
1	5	6	7	2	4	9	8	3
4	7	9	3	8	1	5	6	2
2	8	3	5	6	9	4	1	7
9	2	8	4	7	5	6	3	1
6	3	5	9	1	2	7	4	8
7	1	4	8	3	6	2	9	5

SUDOKU #157

1	6	9	4	8	7	3	2	5
7	5	4	1	2	3	6	8	9
8	2	3	5	9	6	4	7	1
2	9	1	3	4	8	5	6	7
3	8	5	7	6	1	2	9	4
6	4	7	2	5	9	8	1	3
9	3	2	6	1	4	7	5	8
4	1	6	8	7	5	9	3	2
5	7	8	9	3	2	1	4	6

SUDOKU #158

8	2	1	5	9	3	7	6	4
9	7	4	8	6	1	5	3	2
6	5	3	7	4	2	1	9	8
4	1	5	9	2	6	3	8	7
7	3	6	1	8	4	9	2	5
2	8	9	3	5	7	4	1	6
5	6	2	4	3	9	8	7	1
3	4	7	6	1	8	2	5	9
1	9	8	2	7	5	6	4	3

SUDOKU #159

1	3	2	4	9	6	7	5	8
9	6	5	7	8	2	1	3	4
4	8	7	1	5	3	9	6	2
8	2	1	3	4	7	6	9	5
5	4	9	8	6	1	2	7	3
6	7	3	9	2	5	4	8	1
2	1	6	5	7	8	3	4	9
3	9	8	6	1	4	5	2	7
7	5	4	2	3	9	8	1	6

SUDOKU #160

1	7	2	6	5	8	4	3	9
9	3	6	1	7	4	8	2	5
5	8	4	2	3	9	6	7	1
3	2	9	5	4	1	7	8	6
6	4	8	9	2	7	1	5	3
7	5	1	3	8	6	9	4	2
2	6	7	8	1	3	5	9	4
8	1	5	4	9	2	3	6	7
4	9	3	7	6	5	2	1	8

SUDOKU #161

1	8	2	3	9	5	7	6	4
9	6	5	2	7	4	1	3	8
3	4	7	1	8	6	9	5	2
5	1	3	7	6	2	4	8	9
7	9	4	5	3	8	2	1	6
6	2	8	4	1	9	5	7	3
4	5	1	8	2	3	6	9	7
8	7	9	6	4	1	3	2	5
2	3	6	9	5	7	8	4	1

SUDOKU #162

3	6	9	5	7	4	8	1	2
5	8	2	1	6	3	7	4	9
1	4	7	9	8	2	5	6	3
9	5	4	3	2	6	1	7	8
7	1	8	4	9	5	3	2	6
2	3	6	8	1	7	9	5	4
8	2	3	7	4	1	6	9	5
6	9	1	2	5	8	4	3	7
4	7	5	6	3	9	2	8	1

SUDOKU #163

8	2	7	3	6	9	1	4	5
5	4	9	8	1	7	6	2	3
1	3	6	4	5	2	7	9	8
4	5	1	2	9	6	8	3	7
2	9	8	1	7	3	4	5	6
6	7	3	5	4	8	2	1	9
7	6	2	9	3	4	5	8	1
9	8	5	6	2	1	3	7	4
3	1	4	7	8	5	9	6	2

SUDOKU #164

9	3	6	5	4	7	2	8	1
1	8	4	9	2	6	3	5	7
5	2	7	3	1	8	4	9	6
7	1	2	4	9	3	8	6	5
3	6	9	8	7	5	1	2	4
4	5	8	2	6	1	9	7	3
6	7	3	1	8	2	5	4	9
2	9	1	6	5	4	7	3	8
8	4	5	7	3	9	6	1	2

SUDOKU #165

9	2	3	7	6	1	4	8	5
6	4	8	5	9	2	7	1	3
7	1	5	4	3	8	2	9	6
3	9	1	2	5	4	6	7	8
5	7	2	6	8	9	3	4	1
4	8	6	3	1	7	5	2	9
2	3	9	8	4	5	1	6	7
1	6	7	9	2	3	8	5	4
8	5	4	1	7	6	9	3	2

SUDOKU #166

3	2	9	8	6	7	5	4	1
5	6	7	4	3	1	2	9	8
1	8	4	2	5	9	7	6	3
4	7	6	5	8	3	9	1	2
9	3	2	1	7	6	4	8	5
8	5	1	9	4	2	3	7	6
6	4	5	7	2	8	1	3	9
2	1	3	6	9	4	8	5	7
7	9	8	3	1	5	6	2	4

SUDOKU #167

1	2	5	8	3	6	7	9	4
8	7	3	4	5	9	6	1	2
4	9	6	1	7	2	8	5	3
7	5	4	2	8	1	9	3	6
6	1	8	3	9	7	2	4	5
9	3	2	6	4	5	1	8	7
5	4	9	7	2	8	3	6	1
2	8	1	5	6	3	4	7	9
3	6	7	9	1	4	5	2	8

SUDOKU #168

7	9	6	4	1	5	3	2	8
1	3	5	8	6	2	4	9	7
8	4	2	3	9	7	6	1	5
3	6	9	2	5	1	8	7	4
5	2	8	6	7	4	9	3	1
4	1	7	9	3	8	2	5	6
6	5	3	7	8	9	1	4	2
9	7	4	1	2	6	5	8	3
2	8	1	5	4	3	7	6	9

SUDOKU #169

3	7	2	1	5	6	8	4	9
5	4	6	7	9	8	3	2	1
9	1	8	3	2	4	7	6	5
7	8	4	5	6	9	2	1	3
2	5	3	4	8	1	6	9	7
1	6	9	2	7	3	5	8	4
6	3	7	9	4	2	1	5	8
8	9	5	6	1	7	4	3	2
4	2	1	8	3	5	9	7	6

SUDOKU #170

4	2	1	8	9	6	3	5	7
6	3	5	7	2	1	8	4	9
8	7	9	4	5	3	2	6	1
3	6	8	9	7	5	1	2	4
1	5	7	2	3	4	6	9	8
9	4	2	1	6	8	5	7	3
2	1	4	5	8	9	7	3	6
5	9	3	6	1	7	4	8	2
7	8	6	3	4	2	9	1	5

SUDOKU #171

7	3	6	4	2	8	5	1	9
9	5	2	6	1	3	8	4	7
8	1	4	9	7	5	3	2	6
4	2	1	7	3	6	9	5	8
6	9	7	8	5	4	1	3	2
5	8	3	1	9	2	6	7	4
2	6	8	3	4	1	7	9	5
1	7	5	2	6	9	4	8	3
3	4	9	5	8	7	2	6	1

SUDOKU #172

5	9	7	2	6	8	1	4	3
1	6	3	4	7	5	9	2	8
8	2	4	1	9	3	5	7	6
2	3	9	7	4	1	6	8	5
6	5	1	9	8	2	4	3	7
7	4	8	3	5	6	2	1	9
3	8	5	6	1	4	7	9	2
4	7	6	8	2	9	3	5	1
9	1	2	5	3	7	8	6	4

SUDOKU #173

8	6	3	7	9	4	1	2	5
1	2	9	5	6	3	7	8	4
4	7	5	2	8	1	6	9	3
9	4	7	8	1	2	5	3	6
2	5	6	3	7	9	4	1	8
3	1	8	6	4	5	9	7	2
7	8	2	1	5	6	3	4	9
5	3	4	9	2	7	8	6	1
6	9	1	4	3	8	2	5	7

SUDOKU #174

2	3	6	1	7	9	8	4	5
9	4	1	5	8	6	7	2	3
5	7	8	3	4	2	1	6	9
7	1	5	2	6	8	9	3	4
4	6	2	9	1	3	5	7	8
8	9	3	7	5	4	2	1	6
6	8	9	4	2	1	3	5	7
3	2	7	6	9	5	4	8	1
1	5	4	8	3	7	6	9	2

SUDOKU #175

1	4	7	3	9	5	6	2	8
6	8	3	4	2	7	1	5	9
2	5	9	8	6	1	3	7	4
3	6	8	7	1	4	2	9	5
9	7	5	6	3	2	4	8	1
4	2	1	5	8	9	7	6	3
8	3	4	2	5	6	9	1	7
5	9	6	1	7	3	8	4	2
7	1	2	9	4	8	5	3	6

SUDOKU #176

5	8	9	2	4	3	6	7	1
3	1	4	9	6	7	8	5	2
2	6	7	1	8	5	4	9	3
8	9	3	4	2	1	7	6	5
6	4	2	7	5	9	1	3	8
1	7	5	8	3	6	9	2	4
7	2	1	3	9	8	5	4	6
9	3	6	5	1	4	2	8	7
4	5	8	6	7	2	3	1	9

SUDOKU #177

8	4	3	5	7	9	2	1	6
9	1	7	2	6	3	5	8	4
5	2	6	1	8	4	7	3	9
4	7	9	3	2	8	6	5	1
3	5	8	6	1	7	4	9	2
1	6	2	9	4	5	8	7	3
6	3	4	8	5	1	9	2	7
2	9	5	7	3	6	1	4	8
7	8	1	4	9	2	3	6	5

SUDOKU #178

6	9	7	4	3	1	8	2	5
3	8	5	2	9	7	1	6	4
1	2	4	6	8	5	3	7	9
4	1	9	8	7	2	5	3	6
7	6	2	3	5	4	9	1	8
8	5	3	9	1	6	7	4	2
5	3	6	7	4	8	2	9	1
2	7	1	5	6	9	4	8	3
9	4	8	1	2	3	6	5	7

SUDOKU #179

6	5	3	1	4	9	2	7	8
7	4	8	5	6	2	3	1	9
2	1	9	3	8	7	4	5	6
5	9	7	8	3	1	6	4	2
3	2	6	4	7	5	8	9	1
4	8	1	9	2	6	7	3	5
8	3	5	6	9	4	1	2	7
9	6	2	7	1	3	5	8	4
1	7	4	2	5	8	9	6	3

SUDOKU #180

2	4	6	8	9	5	3	7	1
3	5	8	1	7	2	9	6	4
9	7	1	4	3	6	8	5	2
7	6	2	3	4	8	5	1	9
8	1	3	5	6	9	4	2	7
4	9	5	2	1	7	6	8	3
5	8	9	7	2	4	1	3	6
6	3	7	9	8	1	2	4	5
1	2	4	6	5	3	7	9	8

SUDOKU #181

4	9	1	3	2	5	7	8	6
2	3	7	4	8	6	1	9	5
6	8	5	7	1	9	4	2	3
8	7	2	5	3	1	9	6	4
5	1	6	9	4	8	2	3	7
3	4	9	6	7	2	5	1	8
1	2	4	8	5	3	6	7	9
7	6	3	2	9	4	8	5	1
9	5	8	1	6	7	3	4	2

SUDOKU #182

1	4	5	7	2	8	6	3	9
8	3	7	9	6	4	2	1	5
6	9	2	1	3	5	4	7	8
9	8	1	4	7	2	3	5	6
2	6	3	5	8	9	1	4	7
7	5	4	6	1	3	8	9	2
3	7	6	2	5	1	9	8	4
5	1	9	8	4	6	7	2	3
4	2	8	3	9	7	5	6	1

SUDOKU #183

6	2	3	4	8	9	1	7	5
8	9	1	6	7	5	3	2	4
7	5	4	2	3	1	6	9	8
5	7	8	3	4	6	9	1	2
1	4	2	9	5	7	8	6	3
9	3	6	1	2	8	5	4	7
2	6	5	7	9	3	4	8	1
4	8	9	5	1	2	7	3	6
3	1	7	8	6	4	2	5	9

SUDOKU #184

9	8	3	2	1	4	5	6	7
4	5	1	7	9	6	2	3	8
6	2	7	5	8	3	4	9	1
8	1	2	9	5	7	6	4	3
5	3	4	8	6	1	9	7	2
7	6	9	4	3	2	8	1	5
2	7	8	3	4	9	1	5	6
3	4	6	1	2	5	7	8	9
1	9	5	6	7	8	3	2	4

SUDOKU #185

3	6	7	1	9	4	2	5	8
8	2	9	5	7	3	1	4	6
5	4	1	6	8	2	7	3	9
2	7	3	4	6	8	5	9	1
1	9	8	2	3	5	4	6	7
4	5	6	7	1	9	8	2	3
6	8	2	9	4	1	3	7	5
7	1	5	3	2	6	9	8	4
9	3	4	8	5	7	6	1	2

SUDOKU #186

3	5	8	9	1	6	2	4	7
6	4	7	8	3	2	9	1	5
1	2	9	7	5	4	6	3	8
7	3	5	1	6	9	4	8	2
2	1	4	3	7	8	5	9	6
9	8	6	2	4	5	1	7	3
4	9	2	6	8	7	3	5	1
8	6	3	5	9	1	7	2	4
5	7	1	4	2	3	8	6	9

SUDOKU #187

8	3	5	7	4	6	2	9	1
4	9	1	8	2	5	7	6	3
7	2	6	1	9	3	8	4	5
9	8	4	5	3	2	1	7	6
1	6	3	9	7	8	5	2	4
5	7	2	6	1	4	3	8	9
2	1	8	4	5	9	6	3	7
3	4	7	2	6	1	9	5	8
6	5	9	3	8	7	4	1	2

SUDOKU #188

5	2	3	6	7	4	8	1	9
9	7	4	1	2	8	5	3	6
8	1	6	9	5	3	7	4	2
4	9	8	3	1	5	6	2	7
7	5	2	8	4	6	1	9	3
6	3	1	2	9	7	4	8	5
2	8	9	5	6	1	3	7	4
1	6	7	4	3	2	9	5	8
3	4	5	7	8	9	2	6	1

SUDOKU #189

3	5	1	9	2	6	4	8	7
4	8	6	3	5	7	2	9	1
9	2	7	1	4	8	6	3	5
6	9	5	8	1	3	7	4	2
1	7	2	6	9	4	8	5	3
8	3	4	2	7	5	1	6	9
5	4	9	7	8	2	3	1	6
7	6	8	5	3	1	9	2	4
2	1	3	4	6	9	5	7	8

SUDOKU #190

2	7	3	1	9	8	4	6	5
9	8	5	6	7	4	1	3	2
6	1	4	5	2	3	7	8	9
7	4	1	3	6	2	9	5	8
5	9	6	8	4	7	2	1	3
3	2	8	9	1	5	6	4	7
1	3	2	4	5	9	8	7	6
4	5	7	2	8	6	3	9	1
8	6	9	7	3	1	5	2	4

SUDOKU #191

4	5	8	2	9	1	3	7	6
1	6	3	5	8	7	4	2	9
2	7	9	6	3	4	8	1	5
6	3	7	8	4	2	5	9	1
5	9	2	1	7	3	6	4	8
8	4	1	9	5	6	2	3	7
9	1	6	3	2	5	7	8	4
3	8	4	7	6	9	1	5	2
7	2	5	4	1	8	9	6	3

SUDOKU #192

5	2	3	7	9	8	6	1	4
7	6	1	2	4	3	8	9	5
8	4	9	6	5	1	7	3	2
1	5	4	3	8	6	9	2	7
2	3	6	9	7	4	5	8	1
9	8	7	5	1	2	4	6	3
3	7	5	1	6	9	2	4	8
4	9	2	8	3	5	1	7	6
6	1	8	4	2	7	3	5	9

SUDOKU #193

2	1	9	5	8	6	4	3	7
6	5	3	4	7	9	8	1	2
4	7	8	3	2	1	9	5	6
8	4	6	9	1	3	2	7	5
1	3	7	2	5	4	6	9	8
5	9	2	7	6	8	1	4	3
3	8	4	6	9	7	5	2	1
7	6	5	1	4	2	3	8	9
9	2	1	8	3	5	7	6	4

SUDOKU #194

2	4	1	3	8	6	5	7	9
5	9	6	2	7	1	4	3	8
8	3	7	4	5	9	2	6	1
9	8	5	7	4	2	3	1	6
3	7	4	1	6	5	8	9	2
1	6	2	9	3	8	7	5	4
6	2	3	8	9	7	1	4	5
7	1	9	5	2	4	6	8	3
4	5	8	6	1	3	9	2	7

SUDOKU #195

3	5	6	7	4	8	9	2	1
2	4	9	6	3	1	8	7	5
8	7	1	9	5	2	6	3	4
9	2	8	1	7	5	3	4	6
5	1	7	4	6	3	2	9	8
4	6	3	2	8	9	1	5	7
1	3	5	8	2	4	7	6	9
6	9	2	5	1	7	4	8	3
7	8	4	3	9	6	5	1	2

SUDOKU #196

6	2	9	3	1	5	8	7	4
7	3	8	4	6	9	2	5	1
5	4	1	7	8	2	6	3	9
1	9	2	8	7	4	5	6	3
8	6	5	1	2	3	4	9	7
3	7	4	5	9	6	1	2	8
4	5	7	6	3	1	9	8	2
2	8	6	9	4	7	3	1	5
9	1	3	2	5	8	7	4	6

SUDOKU #197

8	1	5	9	3	2	4	6	7
3	4	9	6	7	8	1	2	5
2	6	7	4	1	5	8	9	3
1	7	3	2	5	4	9	8	6
9	5	2	7	8	6	3	1	4
4	8	6	1	9	3	7	5	2
5	3	4	8	2	1	6	7	9
7	2	1	3	6	9	5	4	8
6	9	8	5	4	7	2	3	1

SUDOKU #198

6	5	3	4	2	1	9	8	7
8	9	1	5	6	7	4	3	2
2	7	4	9	3	8	5	6	1
5	6	7	8	1	4	2	9	3
3	1	8	2	9	5	7	4	6
4	2	9	3	7	6	1	5	8
7	3	6	1	4	9	8	2	5
1	4	5	6	8	2	3	7	9
9	8	2	7	5	3	6	1	4

SUDOKU #199

9	3	2	7	4	8	6	5	1
1	7	4	5	2	6	9	3	8
8	6	5	1	3	9	2	4	7
4	8	3	9	7	5	1	6	2
2	5	9	3	6	1	7	8	4
7	1	6	4	8	2	3	9	5
6	2	1	8	9	4	5	7	3
3	9	8	2	5	7	4	1	6
5	4	7	6	1	3	8	2	9

SUDOKU #200

9	4	1	3	7	8	5	2	6
3	5	7	2	6	4	1	9	8
2	6	8	9	5	1	7	4	3
4	1	6	8	3	5	9	7	2
5	2	3	7	4	9	8	6	1
8	7	9	1	2	6	3	5	4
6	9	5	4	1	3	2	8	7
7	3	4	5	8	2	6	1	9
1	8	2	6	9	7	4	3	5